Watching the Weather

WATCHING
THE WEATHER

JOHN & MARY GRIBBIN

CONSTABLE · LONDON

First published in Great Britain 1996
by Constable and Company Limited
3 The Lanchesters, 162 Fulham Palace Road
London W6 9ER

Copyright © John & Mary Gribbin 1996
The right of John & Mary Gribbin to be identified
as the authors of this work has been asserted by them
in accordance with the Copyright, Designs and Patents Act 1988

ISBN 0 09 476530 8

A CIP catalogue record for this book
is available from the British Library

Typeset in Sabon by
Rowland Phototypesetting Limited
Bury St Edmunds, Suffolk
Printed and bound in Great Britain by
St Edmundsbury Press Limited
Bury St Edmunds, Suffolk

CONTENTS

ACKNOWLEDGEMENTS

This book has grown out of our regular contributions to the 'Weatherwatch' column in the *Guardian*. We are grateful to Tim Radford for initiating this series of mini-articles, Celia Locks for persevering with it and Carol O'Brien for suggesting that we turn it into a book.

John & Mary Gribbin
May 1996

INTRODUCTION

The life zone on Earth is small. The average distance from the top of the tallest mountain on Earth to the bottom of the deepest ocean trench is only about 20 km, a distance which, in horizontal terms, you could cover in about ten minutes by car, and which represents less than a gentle day's walking. If the Earth were reduced to the size of a basketball, the 'green smear' representing the life zone would be a film just half a millimetre thick over the surface of the ball. The breathable atmosphere represents just half this life zone, and it affects just about everything we do.

The atmosphere is today made up of roughly 75 per cent molecular nitrogen, 23 per cent molecular oxygen, 1 per cent water vapour and 1.3 per cent argon, by mass (the corresponding figures by volume are slightly greater for nitrogen and slightly smaller for the other main constituents). There are traces (less than 0.1 per cent by mass) of carbon dioxide, neon, helium, methane, krypton, carbon monoxide and sulphur dioxide, with even smaller traces (less than 0.0001 per cent by mass) of molecular hydrogen, nitrous oxide, ozone, xenon, nitrogen dioxide, radon and nitric oxide.

The overall structure of the lower atmosphere is a series of layers in which the layer nearest the ground, the troposphere, and the layer just above, the stratosphere, play key roles in determining patterns of weather and climate, and have the biggest direct influence on life on Earth. This layered structure can best be seen by looking at how the temperature of the atmosphere varies with height above the surface of the Earth.

The source of energy that warms the atmosphere is (apart from a tiny amount of geothermal energy, which can be ignored) heat from the Sun, in the form of electromagnetic radiation. Most of the Sun's energy is radiated in the visible part of the spectrum, between 0.4 and 0.7 micrometres; this is why it is visible: our eyes have evolved to make use of what is available. This radiation passes through the atmosphere without being absorbed and warms the surface of the Earth. About 7 per cent of the Sun's energy is radiated at shorter wavelengths, below 0.4 micrometres, in the ultraviolet. This radiation is absorbed by molecules of oxygen and ozone in the stratosphere and warms that layer directly. A little solar energy is radiated at longer wavelengths, above 0.7 micrometres, in the infrared. Some of this is absorbed in the atmosphere, but it plays only a very minor part in keeping the air warm.

The atmosphere is primarily heated from below, by the warm surface of the Earth. This is partly due to the direct conduction of heat from the warm surface to the gas above it, but it is mainly because the warm surface of the Earth radiates in the infrared part of the spectrum, and infrared radiation is absorbed by molecules such as water vapour and carbon dioxide in the lower atmosphere. The infrared radiation that is absorbed in the lowest layer of the atmosphere makes the air warm, so the air itself radiates heat in turn, still at infrared wavelengths. Some of this radiation goes back down to the surface and keeps it warmer than it would otherwise be. This is the so-called 'greenhouse effect'. The rest works its way upwards through the atmosphere, being absorbed and re-radiated successively until it eventually escapes into space.

The warmth of the lowest layer of the atmosphere causes convection, because the heated air expands, becoming less dense than the cooler air above it, and rises. This is a key process in the determination of weather and climate, contributing to the overall circulation of the atmosphere. But the warm air cannot rise upward to the top of the atmosphere because it is held down within the troposphere by the presence of warmer air in the stratosphere above. The stratosphere – which is essentially synonymous with the ozone layer – is the region where direct solar heating occurs as ultraviolet radiation is absorbed. Ozone, a tri-atomic form of oxygen, is produced in the atmosphere by the effect of ultraviolet radiation on ordinary di-atomic oxygen molecules, splitting them apart and providing single oxygen atoms that can attach to other di-atomic molecules. The ozone itself also absorbs ultraviolet radiation, at slightly different wavelengths. Both processes extract energy from the solar radiation passing through the atmosphere, and thereby warm the stratosphere.

The stratosphere can be thought of as a lid on the troposphere, holding down convection and keeping weather confined within the lowest layer of the stratosphere; it operates in this way because the stratosphere is an inversion layer, in which temperature increases with height and therefore convection cannot occur.

The average temperature at the surface of our planet is about 15 °C, which is some 33 °C warmer than it would be if the Earth had no blanket of air, and therefore no greenhouse effect, to keep it warm. Rising through the troposphere, the temperature initially falls with increasing altitude by about 6 °C for every kilometre. The fall slows at a height of about 10 km and stops altogether at 15 km. This is the boundary between the troposphere and the stratosphere, known as the tropopause. The exact height of the tropopause varies with latitude, with the seasons and from day to night, so the numbers given here are only approximate. The troposphere contains about 75 per cent of the atmosphere of the Earth by mass; at the tropopause, the density of the atmosphere is about 25 per cent of the density at sea level.

The simplest definition of climate is the 'average weather' of a region. Some regions experience much the same temperature throughout the year, others have hot summers and cold winters; some regions are likely to experience rainfall in any month, others have well-defined wet seasons, and so on. The energy that drives all these weather patterns comes from the Sun and is absorbed on Earth mainly in the tropics, near the equator. Some of the energy is then distributed to higher latitudes by the circulation of the atmosphere and the oceans, and these are strongly affected by the geographical distribution of land and sea, the tilt of the Earth, and the way it spins on its axis.

The Earth is a roughly spherical planet orbiting the Sun in a roughly circular orbit once every year. Although the orbit is slightly elliptical, so that in some months we are a little closer to the Sun than in other months, this is not the cause of seasonal variations in weather. If it were, the entire globe would experience winter at the same time; in fact, the closest approach to the Sun now occurs during northern hemisphere winter.

If our planet were a uniform sphere, spinning with its axis vertical relative to a line joining the centre of the Earth to the centre of the Sun, it would experience a very simple pattern of atmospheric circulation. This idealised pattern is the basis for understanding the actual circulation of the atmosphere, and it is driven by the difference in solar heating between the tropics and the poles.

Because the curvature of the Earth makes the planet's surface slope away from the Sun on either side of the equator, the amount of incoming solar energy that falls on a square metre of the Earth's surface at the equator is spread over a successively larger area at successively greater distances from the equator. So higher latitudes are cooler than low latitudes, in exactly the same way that the warming effect of the Sun is less early in the morning or late in the evening, when its rays strike the ground at a shallow angle, than at noon, when it is high overhead.

Incoming solar energy is mainly at visible wavelengths, which are not absorbed in the Earth's atmosphere. When this radiation warms the surface of the Earth, the surface radiates energy in its turn, but at longer wavelengths, chiefly in the infrared. Much of this energy is absorbed in the lower atmosphere, which is warmed as a result by the so-called 'greenhouse effect'. This initiates convection.

Warm air rising near the equator cools and moves outward at high altitudes before descending again in the region around 30 degrees of latitude on either side of the equator. Surface-level winds return air towards the equator to replace the rising air, completing a circulation pattern known as the Hadley Cell, after the eighteenth-century meteorological pioneer George Hadley.

Poleward of the region dominated by Hadley-type circulation, the pattern of atmospheric convection is more complicated, but as a rough guide it can be thought of in terms of two further cells in each hemisphere. Overall, warm air is transferred poleward and is replaced by cold air moving towards the equator. Rising air is associated with low pressure at the surface and produces rain as the rising air cools; descending air is associated with high pressure at the surface, and is dry. Even such a simple picture of atmospheric circulation can explain broad features of climate, such as the warm, wet tropics and the desert regions just outside the tropics. But even on this idealised picture, surface winds do not blow due north–south, because of the rotation of the Earth.

Each point on the surface of the Earth completes one rotation in twenty-four hours. Near the poles, this involves describing a tiny circle at a very slow linear speed; at the equator it involves a speed of 470 metres per second, and at a latitude of 60 degrees a linear speed of 224 metres per second, always from west to east. Air that originates near the equator and is carried poleward by convection carries with it a memory of the high west–east speed it starts out with, and when it returns to the surface it is moving eastward faster than it should be at that latitude. So the surface winds blowing poleward from the equatorial region are deflected to the east. This is why the prevailing pattern of weather at the latitudes of Britain or New Zealand, for example, brings weather systems from the west.

Similarly, air returning towards the equator at low level is imprinted with the linear speed associated with the rotation at higher latitudes. In effect, these prevailing winds – the trade winds – are being overtaken by the surface of the rotating Earth as they move to lower latitudes, so that instead of blowing at right angles to the equator they blow diagonally from the east.

The equator they blow towards, however, is the 'meteorological' equator, where the Sun is directly overhead at noon. The latitude where this occurs changes during the year, causing seasonal variations in climate, because the Earth is actually tilted at 23.5 degrees out of the perpendicular in its orbit around the Sun. The hemisphere that is tilted towards the Sun is warmed more intensely, both because the Sun rises higher in the sky and because the Sun is above the horizon for more than twelve hours each day. In the opposite hemisphere, the noonday Sun is lower on the horizon at corresponding latitudes, and there are more than twelve hours of night. Because the Earth maintains its orientation in space as it orbits the Sun, northern and southern hemispheres each experience summer and winter in turn.

Between latitude 23.5° N (the Tropic of Cancer) and latitude 23.5° S (the Tropic of Capricorn), the Sun will be directly overhead at noon on at least one day in the year. Outside the tropics this never happens. The Sun is overhead at the Tropic of Cancer at noon on 22–3 June each year, and overhead at the Tropic of Capricorn on 22–3 December. Halfway between these dates, the noonday Sun is overhead at the equator, and the whole planet experiences twelve hours of day and twelve hours of night. The atmospheric circulation pattern has to adjust constantly to the resulting changes in the energy balance of the planet.

Further complications to the simple circulation pattern are caused by the presence of mountains, deflecting low-level winds, and by the different ways in which oceans, land and ice-caps respond to the warming influence of the Sun. But the other major influence on climate is the circulation of the oceans.

The great surface ocean currents are generated by the influence of the prevailing winds, blowing steadily across the sea. Like the atmospheric circulation, the currents are influenced by the rotation of the Earth, but unlike the winds they are completely unable to cross land masses. So the dominant pattern of surface ocean currents is a roughly circular flow, or gyre, within each of the great ocean basins. The sweep of these currents is clockwise in the northern hemisphere and anticlockwise in the southern. The main exception to this pattern is the circumpolar current that flows completely around Antarctica from west to east; there is no equivalent current in the northern hemisphere because of the intervening land masses.

Within the circulation of the gyres, water piles up into a dome, so that in the Sargasso Sea, for example, sea level is about a metre higher than on the nearest coast. The effect of the rotation of the Earth is as if there were a force – known as Coriolis force – pushing everything westward, and this piles water up on the western edge of ocean basins, so that sea level in the Caribbean, for example, is slightly higher than on the Pacific side of the Panama Canal. More importantly, this Coriolis effect squeezes the gyres up against the western sides of the ocean basins, producing narrow, fast-flowing currents such as the Gulf Stream. By contrast, the return flow on the eastern sides of the basins is slower and more diffuse.

The Gulf Stream, in particular, transports heat northward and then eastward across the North Atlantic Ocean very efficiently. This is why the British Isles have much milder winters than most regions at comparable latitudes, such as southern Argentina. Other ocean currents are less reliable than the Gulf Stream. The atmospheric and oceanic circulation over the Pacific basin seems to be able to exist in either of two states, one with warm water in the west and cold surface water in the east, and one with the pattern reversed. In either case, the warm region of ocean surface produces a convection pattern with winds blowing into the warm region from the other side of the ocean. These winds push warm surface water into the warm region, exposing colder deep water behind them and maintaining the pattern. But, for reasons that are still not fully understood, from time to time the pattern breaks down and reverses, bringing pronounced changes to the weather of regions as far apart as Australia and South America.

The local phenomenon of a warming of the ocean surface near South America is called El Niño; the overall pattern of changes, which occurs roughly every two years, is called the Southern Oscillation. And there is some evidence that the Southern Oscillation influences weather on a global scale, including the intensity of the African monsoon.

In addition to the influence of its surface currents, the ocean influences climate through its own pattern of convection. Like the atmosphere of the Earth, the ocean is warmed at the surface. But whereas the surface of the Earth is at the bottom of the atmosphere, it is at the top of the ocean. So the water that is warmed by the Sun in the tropics is already at the top of the ocean and cannot rise by convection. Instead, oceanic convection is driven from the polar regions, where cold, salty water sinks down into the depths and makes its way towards the equator.

Wallace Broecker of the Lamont-Doherty Geological Observatory, New York, likens the system to an 'oceanic conveyor belt', which at present works to the benefit of the North Atlantic. The surface currents that bring warm water to the North Atlantic can be traced all the way back to the Indian and Pacific oceans. The water gives up its heat to cold winds blowing across the North Atlantic from Canada and sinks, starting the upside-down convection of the deep ocean current systems. The amount of heat it gives up is nearly one-third as much each year as the region receives from the Sun; this mainly benefits Europe, which is downwind of the ocean. Cold, deep currents then carry the circulation back into the Indian and Pacific oceans, where the water rises once more (pushed by the flow behind it) and warms as it begins the long journey back to the North Atlantic.

The pattern is maintained by salt. Because the conveyor operates in this way, the North Atlantic is warmer than the North Pacific, so there is proportionately more evaporation there. The water left behind by the evaporation has a higher concentration of salt, so it is denser, which encourages it to sink. The resulting cold, deep flow starts out as the North Atlantic Deep-Water Current, an oceanic 'river' that carries a flow of water twenty times greater than the flow of all the rivers of the world put together. Eventually, it carries salt into the Pacific where it is diluted, reducing the density of the water in the flow.

The whole pattern is self-sustaining. But if the conveyor belt were to shut down, the land around the North Atlantic would cool by about 6°C. Furthermore, the pattern would be equally self-stabilising if the conveyor ran in reverse, warming the North Pacific instead of the North Atlantic. Climatologists have found evidence of sudden 'flips' in climate, corresponding to temperature changes of about 6°C, in the geological record of temperature variations during the late stages of the most recent Ice Age, which ended about 15,000 years ago. There is a suggestion – no more than a suggestion at present – that such climate flips may be associated with reversals of the oceanic conveyor belt, like the Southern Oscillation but on a much grander scale. And Broecker has expressed concern that such a flip could happen again, perhaps as a result of human interference with natural climate systems by adding to the burden of greenhouse gases in the atmosphere.

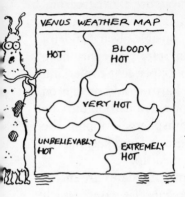

1

ASTRONOMICAL CONNECTIONS

*The usual human perspective on weather is
from the ground upwards, as we showed in
the introduction. But the Earth is a planet, in
a space environment dominated by the Sun.
The Sun controls our weather, and there is
also weather on other planets, and even in
space itself, which puts our parochial
meteorological concerns in a rather different
perspective.*

If the Sun were to cool by just 5 per cent, climatologists
tell us, the Earth would freeze into an Ice Age. Astronomers
assure us that when the Sun was young, some 4,000 million
years ago, it gave out only about three-quarters as much
heat as it does today.

Yet evidence shows that the Earth was warm enough
for liquid water to exist at that time, and that life emerged
in the oceans. This confusing mixture of theories is known
as 'the faint young Sun paradox'.

How can the paradox be resolved? The obvious answer
is the greenhouse effect. Greenhouse gases, including carbon
dioxide, in the primeval atmosphere of our planet could

have trapped heat and kept the temperature above freezing.

Carbon dioxide itself, however, the archetypal green-house gas, was probably not responsible. Ken Caldeira and James Kasting of Pennsylvania State University have recently calculated that, with a Sun 25 per cent cooler and the same atmosphere as today, the Earth would have been so frigid that reflective clouds composed of carbon dioxide ice would have formed in the atmosphere, stopping the Sun's heat from penetrating to the ground and keeping the Earth cool even when the Sun warmed up.

So what did the trick? Two prime candidates are meth-ane and ammonia both effective greenhouse gases, which might have been produced by 'outgassing' from volcanoes when the Earth was young. But then, why didn't the gases trap so much heat when the Sun did warm up that the planet became a desert?

Nobody really knows, but one way or another the Earth has maintained roughly the same temperature for 4,000 million years, while the Sun's output has increased by roughly a third from its original value. A pretty neat trick!

Our planet may not be as significant, on the cosmic scale of things, as the Sun. But it can still influence its nearest neighbour, the Moon.

When rainbows brighten the moon ... It sounds like a line from an old popular song, but it may be factual science. According to C. R. Benn, an astronomer working at the Royal Greenwich Observatory (RGO), the same process that makes rainbows and meteorological haloes on Earth should make the moon brighter at certain times of the month.

Rainbows are produced when droplets of water reflect sunlight internally, bouncing it back at an angle of 138 degrees to the incoming sunlight. The same effect can be seen from an aircraft looking down on the clouds, if the Sun is in the right place, producing a circular 'cloudbow' around the shadow of the aircraft. But in heavy cloud, instead of a coloured circle, the effect becomes a bright white circle, because all the colours of the rainbow are blurred by the cloud and recombined to make white light.

The same effect should, according to C. R. Benn, be visible from the Moon when the cloud around the Earth is in just the right place. At New Moon, when the Sun is shining 'over the Moon's shoulder', the cloudbow effect will make the Earth shine more brightly when a line from the Sun to the Earth and back to the Moon makes an angle of 42 degrees (180 degrees minus 138 degrees).

Strangely, this effect could be seen from Earth. At New Moon, the face of the Moon itself is dark, as seen from Earth, but can often be dimly seen in the reflected light from the Earth (Earthshine). Benn calculates that the cloudbow effect will increase the brightness of the Moon 3.2 days either side of the precise moment of New Moon, and that the effect will last for about half a day.

The snag is that for the effect to be very pronounced, there has to be a lot of cloud cover on Earth, which might make it rather difficult to observe from the ground. However, a satellite in orbit above the clouds could measure the change in lunar brightness linked to the amount of cloud cover on Earth.

There could be a serious side to this kind of study. The amount by which clouds reflect sunlight plays an important part in calculations of how the climate works, and there are few accurate measurements of the size of this effect. Studying moonshine really might lead to a better understanding of clouds and improve those climate models.

*And, of course, the Moon influences the
weather on Earth – in more ways than one.*

Why do cycles of drought and flood in some parts of the
world seem to follow a rhythm nearly twenty years long?
Some researchers have tried to link this to the changing
pattern of the Sun's activity. But Robert Currie thinks that
it is all to do with the Moon.

Currie, an American, is especially interested in the cycle
of droughts in the US Mid-West. When he applied a powerful statistical analysis to the historical record of rainfall
patterns across the region, he was surprised to find an
eighteen-and-a-half-year rhythm affecting its weather. This
matches no known solar cycle, but it almost precisely fits
the movement of the Moon north and south of the equator,
as viewed from Earth. It all has to do with tides produced
in the atmosphere of the Earth, unseen by us, as the Moon
moves through its orbit.

Because the orbit of the Moon around the Earth is tilted
slightly compared with the orbit of the Earth around the
Sun, the Moon seems to weave up and down in the sky,
as well as moving across it. The whole pattern repeats
every 18.6 years, changing the way in which lunar tides
affect the Earth's atmosphere.

Currie argues that the US Mid-West is particularly sensitive to these changes, because it lies downwind in the prevailing westerlies from the Rocky Mountains, which run
more or less north–south up the western side of North
America. The changing lunar tides can tilt the balance
between making the prevailing winds flow north around
the Rockies before sweeping down over the Great Plains
or south around the Rockies before sweeping upwards.
And that, he says, makes all the difference between drought
or plenty, as far as the rainfall of the region is concerned.

The drought pattern matches up with the lunar cycle

back to the beginning of the nineteenth century, although sometimes the drought sets in a couple of years after the lunar tide reaches its maximum. The good news is that the next lunar tidal maximum is not due until the year 2004, so there is plenty of time to make plans.

The Moon also affects the weather with a monthly cycle. In a way, this isn't surprising: if the Moon is going to influence us at all, you might guess it would do so with a monthly rhythm. But how does the influence work?

What could possibly be the cause of a regular monthly variation in average temperatures, affecting the whole world but with the northern and southern hemispheres precisely out of step with each other, and amounting to a full fifth of a degree Celsius? If you've got any idea, the meteorologists would like to hear from you, because they are as baffled by the discovery as everyone else.

The evidence comes from data gathered by the European Centre for Medium-range Weather Forecasting, and covers the five-year period from 1986 to 1991. It essentially gives the temperature everywhere around the world at 1200 GMT each day, and it has been analysed by Clive Best of the Institute for Systems Engineering and Informatics, Ispra, Italy.

The temperature oscillation is stronger nearer the poles and has a period averaging thirty days (plus or minus three days) long. Each day's data is averaged from 51,200 temperature measurements. The variation is almost perfectly sinusoidal, and is bigger in the northern hemisphere, presumably because there is more land there. But because the two hemispheres march out of step, the effect is not obvious in data averaged over the whole globe.

It might be natural to guess that the Moon itself is

somehow responsible for the variation, but there is no obvious way in which it could produce such a large effect. As we have seen, lunar tides raised in the atmosphere of the Earth have been linked with rainfall variations in some parts of the world over a cycle 18.6 years long; but such a regular and relatively large, rapid variation in temperature is hard to explain. One thing is for sure: anybody using these data to study long-term climate change had better take care to subtract out the effect before jumping to any conclusions about global warming.

A heavenly roundabout involving the Moon may be responsible for at least part of the curious monthly cycle of temperature variations. Robert Balling and Randall Cerveny of Arizona State University caused a flurry of meteorological excitement in 1995, when they reported that satellite measurements also show that the average temperature over the whole Earth varies as the Moon waxes and wanes, but only over a range of 0.02 of a degree Celsius. Part of the effect, but not all, can be explained as the warming effect of moonshine itself, helping to keep the chill off the night side of the Earth at times close to full Moon. Now another effect has been found that adds to this full-Moon warming.

Jeppe Dyre of Roskilde University, Denmark, and Coerte Voorhies of the Goddard Spaceflight Center, Greenbelt, Maryland, have independently hit on the same idea, which is to do with the way the Earth and the Moon dance together through space.

Most people think of the Moon as circling around the Earth, forgetting that, as Isaac Newton explained, 'action and reaction are equal and opposite'. So the force of gravity that holds the Moon in orbit around the Earth also acts back upon the Earth itself, with the Moon's gravitational influence tugging the Earth from side to side. The result is that both the Earth and the Moon should properly be regarded as orbiting around their common centre of mass – the point of balance in the Earth–Moon system.

Because the Earth is much more massive than the Moon, the point of balance lies much closer to the centre of the Earth, in exactly the same way that a large adult has to sit very close to the point of balance of a seesaw in order to balance a small child sitting on the far end. Although the distance from the Earth to the Moon is 384,000 km, the distance from the centre of the Earth to the centre around which it orbits in this way is just 4,700 km.

Because the radius of the Earth is 6,368 km, this means that the point of balance actually lies below the surface of the Earth, but that doesn't affect the argument, because the gravitational forces involved act as if all of the mass of the Earth were concentrated at its centre. What matters is the result, namely that we are 9,400 km closer to the Sun at full Moon than we are at new Moon.

The distance to the Sun itself is 150 million km, so the range of the monthly variation is just over 0.006 per cent of the distance to the Sun. This is enough to produce a regular monthly temperature variation of just over 0.008 degrees, about half of the effect discovered by Balling and Cerveny.

If our weather ever gets you down, just take a look at what conditions are like on other planets, and you'll appreciate that things could be a lot worse.

Why is the Earth a comfortable abode for life, while Venus, so nearly its twin in size, is a super-hot desert? Why, come to that, is Mars, only a little further out from the Sun than Earth, a frozen desert?

Take the contrast with Venus first. Earth and Venus are so similar that it is reasonable to assume that they started life in the same way, four billion years ago, when the Sun was young. Initially bare balls of rock, each accumulated an atmosphere rich in carbon dioxide and oceans of water from the gases spewed out by volcanoes. On Earth, the oceans dissolved some carbon dioxide, and more dissolved in rainwater, reacting as it trickled over the surface of the Earth to form limestone rocks.

Carbon dioxide traps heat that would otherwise escape into space; it is a greenhouse gas. So the presence of oceans of water reduced the greenhouse effect and helped to keep the planet cool, even though the Sun warmed.

Venus gets nearly twice as much heat from the Sun as the Earth does. This was just enough, combined with the greenhouse effect of primeval carbon dioxide, to evaporate any primeval oceans as the Sun began to warm. With no way to draw carbon dioxide out of the air, today there is roughly as much carbon dioxide in the atmosphere of Venus as there is in the rocks on Earth. Venus suffers a super-greenhouse effect with temperatures soaring above 500°C.

If only some of that carbon dioxide could have been transported to Mars! There, traces of dried-up water channels show that it, too, started with a rich carbon dioxide atmosphere, a greenhouse effect, and running water. But Mars is further from the Sun than we are and receives less solar heat.

It is also smaller, with a correspondingly weaker gravitational pull, and lost part of its atmosphere into space. Much of the rest got locked up in rocks, weakening the greenhouse effect and freezing the planet.

Like the three bears' porridge, one planet is too hot, another too cold and the third 'just right'. We live on the Goldilocks planet.

*Even on the Goldilocks planet, things have
not always been as pleasant as they are today.*

It stands to reason, common sense might tell us, that Ice
Age winters are cold and harsh, much worse than the winters we experience today. However, in terms of the amount
of heat arriving from the Sun, Ice Age winters ought to be
warmer than those of today. The key to Ice Ages is that
they occur when summers are relatively cool, and (in the
beginning of an Ice Age at least) winters are relatively
mild.

This is because Ice Age rhythms are driven by changes
in the way the Earth moves around the Sun. The orbit of
the Earth changes, stretching to be more elliptical, then
adjusting to be more circular, and the angle of the tilt of
the Earth varies over thousands of years. This tilt, relative
to a line joining the Earth and the Sun, is responsible for
seasons. The hemisphere tilted towards the Sun gets more
heat and light and experiences summer, while the opposite
hemisphere is in the dark of winter.

The changing orbital parameters change the balance of
heat between the seasons, but the amount of heat arriving
at either hemisphere of the Earth from the Sun over a
whole year is always the same. So sometimes severe winters
are offset by warm summers, and sometimes relatively
mild winters 'coincide' with relatively cool summers, for
thousands of years in succession.

The way to make an Ice Age is to have snow on the
ground of the land masses around the Arctic Circle all the
year round. At high latitudes, even during the milder winters it is still cold enough for snow to fall. But it is only
when summers are at their coldest that the snow stays
throughout the year, building up to make great ice sheets.

Once the ice sheets are in place, they reflect away the
incoming solar heat, and chill the planet still further. Both

summers *and* winters then get colder, because so little of the available heat is being absorbed.

The logic applies equally well at the end of an Ice Age. That only happens when the changing balance of the seasons makes summers as hot as possible, while winters are in deep freeze. The ice begins to melt, exposing the dark land beneath, and the dark land absorbs more solar heat, encouraging the ice to melt. At present, the astronomical tendency is for summers to be slowly getting cooler, and winters milder; the next Ice Age is due any millennium now.

It's worth looking a little more closely at the weather on Mars, since it was so nearly a suitable home for life forms like us.

The loss of NASA's Mars *Observer* spaceprobe proved particularly frustrating for researchers at the University of California, Los Angeles. Studying pictures from the *Viking* spacecraft, taken in the 1970s but still providing surprises, they have found the best evidence yet that Mars had a watery past. But there is no immediate prospect of obtaining new data to test their claims.

The idea that Mars once had a relatively warm and wet climate is not new. The surface of the red planet is scoured by channels that look like dried-up river beds.

The favoured explanation for these has been that when the solar system was young, Mars had a thicker atmosphere than it has today, producing a greenhouse effect strong enough to keep the surface temperature above freezing. But Mars is much smaller than Earth, and its gravitational grip has been too weak to hold on to such a thick primordial atmosphere. If the atmosphere ever existed it has largely leaked away into space, reducing the greenhouse effect and cooling the planet into deep freeze as a result.

Although the idea is attractive, the evidence is not yet conclusive, and more is always welcome. The latest comes from studies of a huge crater on Mars, the Argyle Planitia. This is a basin, 1,200 km across and 2 km deep, a flat-bottomed crater produced by an ancient meteor impact.

The UCLA team has found traces of what seem to be channels carved by water flowing out of the basin. The crater lies near the southern polar cap of Mars, and the channels suggest that meltwater from the ice-cap of long ago may have filled the basin before draining out over the edge along the newly discovered channels.

There is still debate about whether the Argyle Planitia could have contained open water or just an ice-covered lake. Either way, the researchers point out that this would be an ideal place to look for signs of life on Mars, since water is an essential requirement of life as we know it.

But was Mars ever really warm and wet? After the *Mariner* orbiter spacecraft sent back pictures of what seemed to be dried-up beds on the Red Planet some twenty-five years ago, many people became excited at the thought that Mars had gone through an Earth-like phase of climate early in its life. This, it was claimed, could have allowed life to develop, and descendants of those life forms might still be around on our planetary neighbour today.

But that prospect has now receded. The only way in which Mars could have been warm enough for rain to fall and lakes (if not seas) to grow would indeed have been if it started out with a thick atmosphere, rich in carbon dioxide, producing a strong greenhouse effect. But astronomers calculate that the Sun was cooler when it was younger, and after many efforts to reconcile the two sets of calculations the experts have had to admit that they don't mesh. When Mars was young, the Sun was so cool that no conceivable greenhouse effect could have made it warm enough for rain to fall.

So where do the channels, clearly cut by flowing liquid on the Martian surface, come from?

The latest ideas suggest that when the Solar System formed, some 4.5 billion years ago, Mars had plenty of water in its crust, but this was locked up in permafrost under weather conditions resembling those of an Arctic winter on Earth today. But before about 3.8 billion years ago, the young planet must have been geologically active, and volcanic heat would have periodically melted large amounts of the ice in local regions.

In addition, the battered face of Mars shows that it was subject to many meteorite impacts in its youth, and these too would have caused local heating, splashing water out to make the river channels before it froze again.

The prospects for finding life on Mars when the next flock of spaceprobes goes to investigate it at the end of the 1990s look more remote than at any time since the early 1970s.

Those meteorite impacts did more than just scar the face of Mars.

Textbooks will tell you that there is no connection between 'meteorites' and 'meteorology', except that both words stem from the Greek *meteoron*, meaning something aloft. Meteorites are lumps of rock from space that fall to Earth, while meteorology is the science of the weather, which goes on aloft in the atmosphere. However, it now seems that there may be a connection between some meteorites and the weather, not on Earth but on Mars.

A few years ago geologists discovered eight meteorites that might have come from Mars. Standard dating techniques showed these rocks to be much younger than most meteorites, and air bubbles trapped inside them had a composition that roughly matched that of the Martian atmosphere analysed by the *Viking* landers.

The claim made at the time was that the impact of a very large meteorite with the surface of Mars itself had, at some time in the relatively recent geological past, blasted fragments of rock clean off the surface of the Red Planet and out into space, where some of them eventually made it to Earth.

This seemed so outrageous that, although the circumstantial evidence was strong, the experts continued to seek confirmation. Now, a team from the University of San Diego and the University of Hawaii has found a closer match than ever before between the composition of the bubbles of air trapped in some of these meteorites and the composition of the Martian atmosphere. The match is so precise that there is now no room to doubt the Martian origin of the meteorites.

This brings us back to the weather of Mars. As well as bubbles of air, some of the meteorites contain drops of water. Today, Mars is a cold, desiccated planet. Any water it possesses must be in the form of ice. But the huge dried-up water courses show that long ago water ran freely on the surface of Mars and that it must have experienced clouds and rain at that time. The droplets in the Martian meteorites are fossil traces of this ancient rain, ice thawed in the meteorite impact and sealed in a rocky receptacle for the voyage across space to Earth.

And weather goes on far beyond the orbit of Mars.

When the probe dropped by the *Galileo* spacecraft sent back data from Jupiter's atmosphere at the beginning of 1996, planetary scientists were initially thrown into confusion. Before the probe burnt out, it sent back data that

showed, among other things, that there was far less water
in the atmosphere than astronomers had predicted. Were
their theories wrong? Had the probe malfunctioned? No.
It now seems that there is a simpler explanation. The probe
encountered an unusually dry part of the Jovian atmosphere, Jupiter's equivalent of a desert.

It may be hard to imagine a planet that is entirely made
of gas having deserts, but the process whereby hot, dry
spots form in the Jovian atmosphere is exactly the same
as the way such deserts as the Sahara form on Earth. Just
as in our own atmosphere, Jupiter's atmosphere is turned
over by convection currents, with hot 'air' rising and cooling before sinking downward again. Both on Earth and on
Jupiter, the rising air loses moisture because water vapour
condenses out of it and forms clouds. Then the high-
altitude dry air is pushed sideways by more air rising from
beneath and sinks downward somewhere else.

The dry, falling air gets hot as it falls, because it is being
compressed by the weight of air behind it. This is exactly
the same as the way a bicycle pump gets hot when you use
it to pump up a tyre, because the air is being compressed.

On Earth, air rises in the tropics, where it is most
strongly heated by the Sun, turns over and falls as hot, dry
air at higher latitudes, including those of the Sahara. On
Jupiter, because there is no solid ground, the hot spots are
not permanent features but come and go as the circulation
changes. On average, they cover a total of just 1 per cent
of Jupiter's surface. It was just bad luck – literally a one
in a hundred chance – that the *Galileo* probe hit one of
these cloud-free deserts.

Thirty times as far from the Sun as the Earth is, the icy
moon Triton orbits its parent planet Neptune. Slightly
closer to the Sun at present, although usually even further
away than Neptune, the frozen planet Pluto orbits around
the Sun. And yet, even so far from any source of warmth,
both Triton and Pluto experience weather, and the nature

of their weather is providing astronomers with insight into how the Solar System formed.

The nature of these distant bodies is revealed by spectroscopic studies using Earth-based telescopes and, in the case of Triton, pictures from the *Voyager* 2 spacecraft. Both are rich in carbon monoxide, which is also found abundantly in clouds of gas and dust between the stars. This supports the idea that the Solar System formed from the collapse of such a cloud.

Pluto's atmosphere also contains methane, as a gas. That in turn implies that the temperature in the atmosphere rises as high as 110K (−163°C) in the warmth of the Sun, even though the temperature on the icy surface of the planet is no more than 50K (−223°C).

Triton, although a moon, has a very thin atmosphere, weather and even seasons. Spectroscopic analysis shows that the icy surface of Triton contains frozen methane, frozen carbon monoxide and frozen nitrogen, at temperatures around 40K. As first one pole of Triton and then the other is warmed by sunlight, these ices sublimate (turning directly from the solid to the gas) and migrate to the colder pole, where they freeze once more.

As well as its unusual composition, Triton has an unusual orbit, circling the 'wrong way' (retrograde) around Neptune. This suggests that it was captured by the gravitational pull of the planet from a cloud of icy objects in the outer reaches of the Solar System. Pluto is probably the largest of these objects, and not a true planet at all.

If these ideas are correct, both Pluto and Triton are representative of the material left over from the formation of the Solar System; they are too far from the Sun to have been altered much by heating and remain frozen fossils of the pre-solar cloud.

And there is even weather in space itself.

Weather in space? It sounds almost a contradiction in terms, but space is far from being a featureless vacuum. Between the stars, there are clouds of gas and dust; conditions within them, especially the temperature, vary widely. This variable interstellar weather is connected with the origins of our Solar System, and maybe of life on Earth.

Even the coldest interstellar clouds are not at absolute zero of temperature, $-273\,°C$ ($0K$). Fifty years ago, astronomers learned from spectroscopic studies that clouds in the depths of space have a temperature of a few K, but they had no idea why. We now know that this is because they are warmed by the famous background of microwave radiation that fills the entire Universe and is evidence of its birth in the Big Bang.

The background radiation is exactly like the radiation in a microwave oven, but colder – a chilly $2.7K$. Interstellar clouds far from any star have the same temperature, proof that they are cooking gently in the microwave oven of the Universe.

But some clouds are much warmer. When stars and planets form, they do so from collapsing clouds of gas and dust. Heat escaping from the proto-stars in the middle warms the surrounding cloud to hundreds of degrees, which makes it radiate energy in the infrared. Infrared telescopes and the satellite IRAS show these hot clouds as stellar nurseries, where planetary systems are being born.

The energy from a nearby star doesn't just warm an interstellar cloud; it also encourages chemical reactions to take place inside it. Complex molecules are built up inside the clouds, and their presence is revealed by their radiation in the radio bands. Molecules such as ammonia and formaldehyde, basic building blocks of life, are commonplace; even more complex molecules are far from rare.

According to one school of thought, soon after the Earth formed and cooled, comets colliding with our planet brought these precursors to life down to the surface, which could explain how life got started on Earth almost as soon as it had cooled. We owe our existence to cosmic rain.

And although the Sun dominates our weather, dramatic changes to terrestrial climate can be caused by visitors from the outer fringes of the Solar System.

Comet Hale-Bopp, heading for a close swing past the Sun in March and April 1997, may provide a spectacular heavenly display to mark the coming end of the millennium, but it may also spread a chill across the world in the early part of the next century.

The problem is that comets are like dirty snowballs made out of a mixture of ice and dust. When the ice thaws during a close approach to the Sun, large amounts of the dust can be released to form a belt girdling the Solar System, and if the Earth passes through such a dust belt, the dust acts as a sunshield, chilling the planet below.

This argument has been around for some time, but has lately been revived by Richard Muller and Gordon MacDonald of the University of California. They got on the trail of such cometary influences on climate through studies of the way the world's weather has changed over the past 600,000 years or so.

During that time, geological evidence shows, the planet has been plunged into a succession of Ice Ages, roughly once every 100,000 years. Muller and MacDonald argue that this is because the tilt of the Earth's orbit around the Sun changes over exactly that timescale, making it wobble up and down slightly.

They have calculated the effect of this wobble, and found

that the cycle exactly matches the climate cycle. As the Earth's orbit moves up and down, every 100,000 years it will happen to lie in exactly the same plane as streams of dust produced by countless comets that have broken up in orbit around the Sun in the past.

Hale-Bopp, however, is a maverick that brings a cooling threat regardless of the rhythm of this long-term cycle. To be seen as bright as it is now, still far out from the Sun, it must be a very large object indeed, carrying a large burden of dust to scatter in the inner Solar System. The link between comet dust and climate may be about to be tested in uncomfortable fashion.

2

THE
CHANGING
CLIMATE

Coming down to Earth again from the depths
of space, we can see how the changing
climate of our planet has played a major part
in shaping our own evolution, and may
explain why we are here at all.

How did human beings get to be among the more successful forms of life on Earth today? We blame the weather
or, if you are going to be strictly accurate about these
things, the changing climate.

About five million years ago, our ancestors were
arboreal, apelike creatures contentedly going about their
business in the forests of East Africa. Then, for reasons
that are still only partly understood, the Earth entered into
a series of recurring Ice Ages. The effect of these climate
changes has been to bring about a cycle in which Ice Ages,
typically a little over 100,000 years long, are separated
by interglacials about 15,000 years long. We live in an
interglacial that began about 15,000 years ago.

Even during a full Ice Age the forests of East Africa
do not freeze, but when the Earth is colder, less water

evaporates from the oceans to fall as rain, and much of the fresh water of the planet is locked up in ice. In East Africa an Ice Age is better described as a dry age.

During the droughts the forests shrank, and the inhabitants had to find another way of life. Some retreated with the forests, becoming even better tree-dwellers. But some moved on to the spreading plains, adapting to a new way of life.

Each time the forest shrank, the apes that were best adapted to the woodland life would continue to do well. But on the edge of the shrinking forest, Darwinian survival of the fittest would operate with full force. Only the most cunning and adaptable individuals would survive. Then, during an interglacial, when the rains returned, the survivors would flourish, reproducing rapidly and building up their population before the next turn of the climate screw.

This repeated tightening of the evolutionary screw and easing off of the pressure could almost have been designed to ensure rapid evolution of intelligence and adaptability. In each dry age, only the most intelligent and adaptable individuals survived, passing on their genes. In the interglacials, the population expanded, spreading those genes. And after a few dozen turns of the screw, in one single interglacial the descendants of all those survivors have exploded in population to dominate the planet.

What happens to the remaining ice-caps of the world today when global temperatures rise? You might think that in a warmer world the ice-caps would melt, shrinking in volume and causing the sea level to rise. You would be wrong. Provided that the polar regions are still cold enough for precipitation to fall as snow, the first thing that happens when the world warms is that the ice-caps get thicker.

The reason is simple. In a warmer world, more water vapour evaporates from the oceans to form clouds and, eventually, to fall as snow or rain. Precipitation is bound to occur over the coldest regions of the globe, where it will fall as snow. So, with increased snowfall each year as the world warms, the ice-caps of Antarctica and Greenland should actually get thicker, even if they are melting back at the edges.

Then things begin to get complicated. A thicker ice-cap is heavier, and this will encourage glaciers to flow more rapidly downhill, carrying the accumulated burden of ice down to the sea, where it can break off and float away in the form of icebergs. It takes thousands of years for snow that falls in the centre of Antarctica to escape from the continent as an iceberg, and because the temperature of the globe is always changing the great ice sheets are never really in equilibrium. The ice-caps today still have a partial memory of the extremely cold and relatively dry conditions some 20,000 years ago, at the end of the latest Ice Age.

Global mean temperatures have increased by about 0.5°C over the present century, and the Greenland ice-cap has indeed been getting thicker at the middle (revealed by radar measurements from satellites) and thinner at the edges in recent decades, which broadly fits the expected pattern for a warming world, whatever the reason for the warming. Overall Greenland is losing a little ice each year, enough to raise sea level by no more than three centimetres in a century.

In Antarctica, equivalent satellite measurements suggest that the balance between snowfall and icemelt is tilted slightly the other way, with Antarctica locking up more frozen water each year and contributing a small net decrease in sea level equivalent to a few centimetres per century. Coincidentally, the two effects, from the northern and southern hemispheres, almost exactly cancel out. The ice-caps are changing as the world warms, but the net effect of those changes is to leave sea level almost unchanged. And yet, as temperatures have increased over the past hundred years, sea level has risen by about 10 centimetres, largely because of the way the sea itself has expanded as temperatures have increased.

*If all that seems to fly in the face of common
sense, try this . . .*

How did an ice-covered country such as Greenland get its
name? The answer may lie in a fluctuation of climate that
took place around the time Iceland and Greenland were
being settled by the Vikings, a little over a thousand years
ago.

Minor variations in climate, slight warmings or coolings
lasting for a few decades or a few centuries, have happened
throughout history. They may be caused by volcanic eruptions, throwing dust high in the air and shielding the surface of the Earth from the Sun, or by changes in the Sun
itself, or by some other, unknown, process. They are
revealed by a variety of geological and other techniques,
including studies of the remains of pollen, seeds and leaves
of plants preserved in ancient sediments.

The spread of Viking voyagers westward around the top
of the Atlantic Ocean took place during a relatively warm
spell (warmer than anything that followed until the present
day) that is known as the North Atlantic optimum and set
in towards the end of the ninth century.

During the 850s, on two separate occasions, Norse voyagers were blown off course and 'discovered' Iceland. The
first attempt at a settlement was led by a farmer, Floki
Vilgerdson, in the 850s, just at the end of a cold spell
lasting several decades. He lost his cattle in a severe winter
and returned home, as the *Landnam Saga* records, with
tales of 'a fjord filled up by sea ice'. And so Iceland got
its name.

Ironically, that is almost the last mention of sea ice in
the area for 300 years. In the 870s, as the world warmed,
other settlers found Iceland more hospitable and colonised
the island in spite of its name.

By the 960s, the colony was so well established that it

was a base for further voyages westward. In 982, Erik the Red, banished for three years for killing two men, headed westward with a shipload of followers and found new land, rugged, mountainous country but with a deep fjord on the south-western coast, warmed by the Gulf Stream (which seems to have pushed more vigorously northward at that time) and with good farming land. Erik called the new land Greenland.

According to the sagas, this was a deliberate confidence-trick to lure new settlers to Erik's colony – an early real estate swindle, but we now know that Erik arrived in Greenland during a particularly warm phase of the climatic optimum, and that the region where he landed was indeed green and fertile at the time.

If Greenland and Iceland had been discovered in the same year by the same explorer, they might well have been given each other's names. One island is indeed covered by ice; the other is more green and fertile. But Iceland was settled at the end of a cold climate fluctuation and Greenland at the peak of a warm climate fluctuation. And that is why Greenland isn't really green in the agricultural sense.

Why do these sorts of changes in climate occur, on a timescale of decades and centuries? One controversial, but intriguing suggestion comes from a most unusual meteorologist.

A less determined man than Goesta Wollin might have given up his studies of the links between magnetism and weather when his first publications on the subject, twenty years ago, met with a decidedly cool response from the scientific community. Scientists poured scorn on his idea that a correlation between weather and the Earth's changing magnetic field could be anything more than a mere

coincidence or statistical fluke. But the detractors should
have realised that a man who, although a Swedish citizen,
chose to join the US Army to fight the Nazis, and whose
first parachute jump was a night drop into Normandy on
the eve of D-Day, as a member of the Intelligence Service
of the 82nd Airborne Division, was unlikely to be put off
by a little academic sniping.

The Earth's magnetic field is always varying; the geological records show that sometimes it has even disappeared
altogether before rebuilding its strength. Wollin has found,
from a variety of geological evidence, that in past epochs
whenever the Earth's magnetic field has been weaker, the
climate of our planet has been warmer. Intrigued by this,
he has looked at how the Earth's magnetic field changes
on much shorter timescales, from year to year and month
to month, and noticed that this, too, ties up with the changing pattern of the weather.

The key to the short-term link between weather and
magnetism turns out to be not simply the strength of the
magnetic field from year to year but the rate at which
the strength is changing. When the magnetic field changes
abruptly, the temperature over the North Pacific region,
in particular, changes measurably (over a range of about
1°C) over the next few years.

Wollin's explanation is that the salty water of the North
Pacific is, unlike pure water, an electrical conductor.
Sweeping clockwise around the ocean basin in a great current, it acts like an electric dynamo, producing a magnetic
field that pushes against the Earth's magnetic field. When
the Earth's magnetic field changes, the feedback between
the changing magnetism and the electricity in the oceans
alters the rate at which the ocean currents are moving,
changing the rate at which warm currents move north
along the coast of Asia and cold currents move south down
the coast of North America, and altering the distribution
of heat around the globe.

As well as holding out the possibility of weather forecasting two or three years in advance, based on observations of the fluctuating magnetic field, Wollin's work gives a whole new meaning to the term 'ocean current'. But don't worry about the possibility of getting a shock if you dip your toe in the briny! The latest measurements show that the electric potential difference between Hawaii and California is a measly couple of volts.

Conventional wisdom has it that even during the height of the latest Ice Age the tropics scarcely felt the chill. But conventional wisdom may be wrong; a study of ice cores drilled from glaciers 6,000 metres above sea level in the Peruvian Andes suggests that, when the high latitudes froze, the tropics also caught a chill.

The discovery is all the more impressive because it wasn't what the weather watchers involved set out to find. Lonnie Thompson from Ohio State University and his colleagues were actually hoping to use subtle changes in the ice to tell them about the behaviour of El Niño, the recurrent shift in weather patterns affecting the Pacific region.

The technique depends on drilling long cores from the ice and analysing the layers laid down from year to year (similar to the annual layers of growth represented by tree rings). This isn't easy in the high Andes: the team used a solar-powered drill that had to be carried up the mountain by a team of thirty porters and forty-four burros. The drill extracted two cores from the ice, one 160 metres long and the other 166 metres long. These then had to be cut up into sections and taken back down the mountain in refrigerated containers for analysis.

The oldest ice is, of course, at the bottom of each core, and Thompson's team were excited to find that chemical analysis showed that the lowest three metres of the cores were between 20,000 and 14,500 years old. That meant that these ice layers were laid down at the end of the latest Ice Age, which ended about 14,000 years ago.

Temporarily abandoning their plans to study El Niño using the upper layers of the ice cores, the team first carried out an analysis of these deeper layers, which was reported in the journal *Science*.

The analysis of the composition of the different layers in the ice cores reveals what the average temperatures were at the time the ice was being laid down in the form of snow. Previously, climatologists thought that even at the height of the Ice Age temperatures in the tropics, at least at sea level, were no more than a couple of degrees cooler than today. But the Andes cores reveal that the air temperature over the mountains must have been at least 8°C lower than today. That corresponds to a cooling of at least 5°C at lower altitudes. The ice layers also contain much more dust than layers from recent times.

The dust suggests why even the tropics were cold at that time. Whatever the reason for the spread of ice near the poles, with more water locked up in ice, the world was much drier during the Ice Age. This encouraged wind-blown dust to spread throughout the atmosphere, acting as a sunshield and cooling the globe even far away from the poles.

Today the amount of dust in the air keeps our planet some 3°C cooler than it would otherwise be, and the Ice Age cores show that 15,000 to 20,000 years ago there was 200 times as much dust in the air as there is today. Computer simulations of past climates will have to be modified to take account of these new discoveries. Meanwhile, Thompson and his colleagues have now gone back to their initial plan and have begun to analyse the upper layers of ice from the same cores to get a picture of how El Niño events have recurred in recent centuries and millennia.

*Dust can also have a smaller, short-term effect
on the weather.*

The eruption of Mount Pinatubo in the Philippines in 1991
brought warnings of severe winters in Europe and North
America as the spreading cloud of stratospheric pollution
from the eruption blocked out incoming sunlight. We
escaped any severe consequences from the eruption,
although climatologists say that the overall effect of the
volcano was to cool the Earth by about half a degree
Celsius, temporarily cancelling out the warming that has
taken place during the twentieth century. As the stratospheric haze cleared, it was a sharp *warming* in the mid-
1990s rather than a sharp *cooling* in 1992–3 that became
the most obvious 'signal' of this particular volcanic influence on our weather.

In the past, however, major volcanic eruptions have
caused severe cold spells, harvest failures and human suf-
fering. The most notorious example occurred in 1816,
which has gone down in history as 'the year without a
summer'. This followed a huge volcanic eruption at Mount
Tambora in Indonesia in 1815. The height of the mountain
was reduced by 1,400 metres, and the eruption ejected an
estimated 100 cubic km of debris, some of which reached
the stratosphere and spread a cooling veil around the globe.

In New England a wave of cold lasting for five days
from 6 June 1816 left several inches of snow on the ground.
A second wave of cold, less severe but even more remarkable so late in the year, struck between 5 and 9 July, killing
what crops had survived the snow. As late as 20 August,
frosts returned in New Hampshire and Maine, and further
south in Massachusetts.

In Europe, struggling to recover from the Napoleonic
wars and with low food reserves, agriculture was wrecked

by bad weather, and many regions of France were affected by famine and rioting.

The most famous volcanic eruption of all, Krakatau in 1883, threw 'only' about 55 cubic km of pollution into the atmosphere, cooling the world by about half a degree for about three to five years, in line with the projections for the influence of Pinatubo. And although individual eruptions great enough to cool the globe are rare, many smaller eruptions going off at about the same time can combine to do the same job. Variations in the amount of volcanic dust in the stratosphere from decade to decade – changes in the so-called Dust Veil Index – may, indeed, account for the occurrence of climatic extremes such as the Little Ice Age of the seventeenth century.

Although it is now well established that the eruption of a large volcano can have a profound effect on weather and climate, it is often forgotten that such an eruption could happen quite close to the British Isles. A new study of environmental changes caused by an Icelandic eruption in the 1780s suggests that there is no cause for complacency.

John Grattan and Mark Brayshaw of the University of Plymouth have been checking out what happened during and after the eruption of the Laki fissure in Iceland between 8 June 1783 and 8 February 1784. The eruption was not particularly violent, but it went on for so long that it poured an enormous amount of polluting material, including acidic droplets, into the air. Then the prevailing weather pattern carried the pollution eastward and dumped it on Europe.

Grattan and Brayshaw have been scouring the printed records of the period, including newspaper accounts, diaries and letters. They have found extensive references, right across Europe, to a persistent smoky fog or haze. In England, the poet William Cowper commented 'we never see the sun but shorn of his beams ... he sets with the face of a red hot salamander and rises with the same complexion', while in Paris Benjamin Franklin, the US

ambassador, not only described the 'persistent fog' which
the Sun could not dissipate but linked it with the Icelandic
eruption.

The haze was noted in Madrid, Paris and Rome. It was
accompanied by intense heat and violent thunderstorms,
while Gilbert White of Selborne described the summer as
an 'amazing and portentous one, and full of horrible
phenomena'.

The full impact on Britain was, says the Plymouth team,
'clearly profound', and included damage to crops, among
them wheat, barley and oats. You thought the summer
of 1995 was a bit extreme? Just wait until the Icelandic
volcanoes erupt again; you ain't seen *nothing* yet!

Dust and magnetism are not the only causes
of climatic change. Hardly surprisingly,
flickers in the Sun itself have a profound effect
on the weather here on Earth. But the
evidence comes from some unexpected places.

Librarians – and householders – tempted to weed out their
old papers to make way for new ones could learn an important lesson from the Armagh Observatory in Northern
Ireland. There, researchers have uncovered a treasure trove
of old weather records going back to 1796. Among other
things, the accurate temperature measurements confirm the
reality of the long-suspected link between solar activity
and the weather.

Established temperature records go back only to 1865,
which is why you should always be a little wary of those
headlines that report the longest drought or the highest
temperature, or whatever, 'on record'. However, in cata-
loguing old material that has literally been gathering dust
at Armagh for decades, astronomers found a sequence of
meteorological data from the late eighteenth and early

nineteenth centuries that links up with the established record and goes back to the 1790s.

One of the first things they were interested in, as astronomers, was the opportunity to test the claim that there is a correlation between solar activity and weather, and this has duly been confirmed. The Sun goes through a more or less regular cycle of activity, roughly eleven years long, but the length of the cycle does vary, and the records show that shorter cycles correspond to higher temperatures on Earth, while more drawn-out cycles are associated with colder temperatures.

Nobody knows exactly how the effect works, but it is certainly something that will have to be taken into account in forecasting future temperature trends.

Moreover, because the climate at Armagh is strongly maritime, the record of temperature variations is in effect a guide to changes going on in the Atlantic Ocean and should give a good average for a large part of the northern hemisphere. It shows a marked warm period from 1840 to 1860, which had not previously been suspected, and pinpoints 1846, the first year of the Great Famine in Ireland, as one of the warmest years on record.

Historians and meteorologists, as well as astronomers and librarians, will be intrigued by the news.

In what ways does the Sun affect the weather on Earth? Apart from the obvious fact that it provides the source of heat that drives the terrestrial weather machine, changes in the Sun over the roughly eleven-year 'sunspot cycle' have also been linked with cyclic changes in temperature and rainfall at various places on Earth, not just Armagh. And yet astronomers will tell you that the output of heat from the Sun does not change enough to explain these changes in the weather.

Perhaps what matters is not the change in *quantity* of radiation coming from the Sun but its changing *quality*. G. A. Nikolsky of St Petersburg University has been carrying out observations of the activity of the Sun since the early 1980s from an observatory more than two kilometres above sea level. He has found that when the Sun is at the most active phase of its cycle, with lots of sunspots to be seen, there are simultaneous bursts of radio noise and blue and ultraviolet light detectable on Earth.

The radio outbursts have long been known and are identified with regions of flaring activity on the surface of the Sun. But Nikolsky has now found that during one of these outbursts, which last for about four hours, the Earth is bathed in blue-ultraviolet light from the sites where all the activity is going on. He suggests that the radiation is coming from a region just below the surface of the Sun, which is exposed by the disturbances at times of flare activity.

Although the surface itself has a temperature of 'only' 5800K (about 5500 degrees on the Celsius scale), the sub-surface layer is as hot as 7800K, which is why it produces this intense radiation.

The effect cannot be observed from sea level, because the blue-ultraviolet radiation is strongly absorbed high above the ground, in the stratosphere. This is equivalent to an input of heat to the stratosphere, which plays an important part in the workings of the weather machine. A small increase in the amount of ultraviolet radiation reaching the stratosphere – equivalent to only a change of 0.1 per cent in the total output from the Sun – can have a large effect on weather patterns around the world.

For the past thirty years, changing water levels in Lake Victoria have also followed the Sun's cycle of activity, as they did between 1900 and 1930, but in the middle third of the present century there was no correlation between sunspots and the lake's level.

This is one of the most baffling of the many alleged influences of solar activity on the weather, but if anything is going to be affected by small changes in climate caused by the activity of the Sun, Lake Victoria is a good candidate.

The lake sits almost exactly on the equator. It is about as big as Ireland and has a catchment area nearly the size of Great Britain. It flows out into the Nile, originally via the Rippon Falls. Although the falls have been drowned by a dam built in 1954, the outflow from the dam is controlled so that it is the same as the outflow was over the falls. The annual outflow has not changed since records began in the late nineteenth century.

The latest study of changing lake levels has been made by Peter J. Mason, a civil engineer with a keen interest in climate cycles. He points out that from 1900 to 1930 lake levels rose when the Sun was active and fell when there were few sunspots over the roughly eleven-year solar cycle. Statistically speaking, the correlation between the two patterns is 0.82, on a scale where 1 would mean that they marched exactly in step.

From 1930 to the end of the 1950s, however, there was no evidence of such a correlation. The equivalent coefficient was 0.07, where 0 would mean there is no agreement between the two records (not that they were running opposite one another; that too would give a coefficient of 1!). Was the earlier agreement just a coincidence?

Perhaps not. Record sunspot activity in 1959 was followed by record high levels of water in the lake, and since then the two have again marched nearly in step, with the correlation back up to 0.65. Since 1900, sunspots seem to have been affecting lake levels more than half the time.

Why? Nobody knows, but if the correlation holds, it could be a useful tool in predicting the availability of water in a region where the resource is scarce. For what it's worth, the Sun should be rising to a new high level of activity over the next few years.

With all this evidence that the Sun's variations affect the weather, it isn't surprising that someone is trying to use solar variations to predict changes in the weather. What is surprising is the way he is doing it.

It takes a brave man to forecast the weather three months in advance, but that's just what Piers Corbyn does.

Corbyn, who trained as an astrophysicist and now runs a company called Weather Action, has long been a thorn in the flesh not just of the Met Office but also the bookies.

He keeps making long-range forecasts that turn out to be accurate often enough to embarrass the traditional forecasters and to provide a steady flow of funds from the bookmaker William Hill into his company's bank account.

But this is not Weather Action's only source of income. The company also provides forecasts for industry, farmers, insurers and organisers of sporting events, most of whom keep coming back for more, so Corbyn must be getting something right.

Exactly what that 'something' is is a closely guarded secret, but Corbyn is happy to let everyone know that it is all based on changes in the Sun's activity. In order to make a forecast, you need to understand how changes in the Sun affect the weather, and then you have to be able to predict the changes in the Sun. So simply telling us that there is a Sun–weather link involved isn't giving too much away.

The solar weather technique is, says Corbyn, particularly good at predicting extreme weather events, which is just where conventional forecasting techniques often fall down.

Ever the maverick, Corbyn also has another shot in his locker. Carbon dioxide in the air does not make the world warmer, he says. Instead, changes in solar activity warm the world, and that brings carbon dioxide out of the oceans and into the air. But, as we shall see, there is very little evidence with which to back this claim.

When the climate does change, even in a small way, it affects life on Earth, not always in predictable ways.

The weather, not pollution, is to blame for the green scum that sometimes spreads across the lakes and ponds. So says M. D. Collins of Nene College, Northampton, after a successful prediction of such an 'algal bloom' in 1994, based on an analysis of conditions in 1989 and 1990.

Those were the most recent occasions when blue-green algae, as they are known, spread in profusion across the lakes of Britain. These algae are important. Without them, we would not be here, since it was their ancestors who first released free oxygen into the air and made it breathable.

Usually these algae are present as part of the ecology of lakes and ponds and cause no problems, but occasionally they form scum on the surface of the water, where aggregates of algae drift together in light winds. The scum can cover the entire surface of a body of water, blocking off light from plants and animals below, and as the algae die and decay they can release toxic chemicals into the water.

The spread of such scum in 1989 and 1990 was widely blamed at the time on run-off of fertilisers from the land, but Collins says that this was not the deciding factor.

Analysis of the weather patterns in central England in those years suggested to Collins that the key factors in causing the bloom were a combination of high temperatures and long hours of sunshine. In both 1989 and 1990 there were eight months of above-average temperatures and hours of sunshine, leading to the development of the scum in the autumn.

This analysis led to the prediction, made on 9 August

1994, when the pattern of sunshine and temperatures had been suitable for scum formation for seven months. The forecast was that if the summer continued fine, algal scum would appear in September and October.

Writing in the journal *Weather* (June 1995), Collins reported that 'an algal problem' did develop in Rutland Water in October 1994, even though a breakdown in the calm conditions stopped the scum from spreading extensively. So farmers should not be blamed for these blooms, and it is worth noting that 1989, 1990 and 1994 were the warmest years on record in southern Britain up to then.

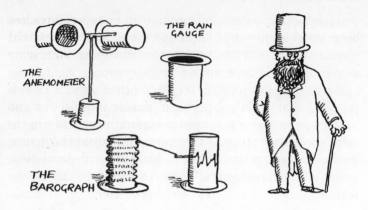

THE RAIN GAUGE

THE ANEMOMETER

THE BAROGRAPH

3 WEATHER PEOPLE

Whatever the causes of changes in weather, they can have a profound effect on people. A bad summer can change an individual's life, for good or ill; and a bad storm can affect the fate of a nation. Then there are those people whose lives get bound up with the weather through no fault of their own.

The United Kingdom owes its existence in large measure to the vagaries of the weather. Our history began, as every schoolchild knows, in 1066, when William, Duke of Normandy, sat throughout the entire month of September with his ships stuck in port by unseasonable bad weather, storms and northerly winds sweeping down the Channel. In England, Harold had gathered an army to await the expected invasion, confident of knocking the Normans back into the sea; but the same winds that kept William bottled up in Normandy blew another fleet of invaders south from Scandinavia to northern England, and Harold was forced to turn his attention to this more immediate threat. The weather changed on 27 September, right at the end of the campaigning season, with southerly winds taking the Norman army over to Sussex in a fleet of 696 ships. Another week, and Harold would have had time to get back from repulsing the invasion of Harold Hardraade in the north, and William would not have got ashore unopposed.

The rest, as they say, is history, but it was by no means all plain sailing. During the Hundred Years War, the British received help from the weather at the Battle of Crécy in 1346 when a storm cleared just in time for the Sun to shine directly into the eyes of the French army, while at Agincourt in 1415 torrential rain turned the battle-field into a mud heap, in which the French horses were soon stuck, making them, and their riders, easy prey for the English bowmen.

In 1588, storms did as much to destroy the attempted invasion by Philip II of Spain as the English navy. A little over two centuries later, Napoleon's advance on Moscow was repelled by the ravages of General Winter. As if that wasn't enough, the weather turned against Napoleon in 1815 at Waterloo, where he delayed his attack, waiting for torrential rain to end. The weather failed to improve, but the delay gave time for the allied forces, under Wellington, to organise themselves.

In the twentieth century, the outcome of great battles again rested on the vagaries of the weather. A large contribution to the 'miracle' of Dunkirk was provided by the fog and flat-calm weather that enabled the flotilla of little ships to rescue more than a quarter of a million men from the beaches. And in the first week of June 1944, the weather was so bad that German forecasters dismissed any possibility of invasion, allowing troops to be stood down from full alert. The invasion took place on D-Day, 6 June, in a 'window' of fine weather successfully predicted by the allied forecasters, who (unlike their German counterparts) had access to meteorological information from out over the Atlantic.

At any of these points, and many others, history could have tilted the other way if the wind had blown from a different direction. But if you are tempted to see this as proof that God is an Englishman, remember that history is written by the victors.

Once the Normans arrived in Britain, they soon made their mark.

Travellers following the course of the River Ouse from Lewes in Sussex down to the sea at Newhaven are often struck by the unusual occurrence of two churches in the space of a few miles whose towers are topped not by the weather-vane but by a weather *fish*. One is at Southover, in Lewes itself, and the other in the village of Piddinghoe, near Newhaven. Both date back to the earliest period of the Norman occupation.

The symbolism of the fish is no mystery, since it was a sign used by early Christians. Just why these two churches should carry the emblem is indeed a mystery. Perhaps there is some significance in the Norman connection – Gundreda, William the Conqueror's niece, is buried in the church at Southover – or perhaps the local fishermen felt the symbol would be more appropriate than the traditional cock.

The question this raises is: why should most other churches have a weather-vane in the form of a cock? Why *is* the cock traditional? This symbol goes back to the ninth century, when a papal decree ordered that all churches should have the figure of a cock set up in the steeple as the emblem of St Peter, a reference to his denial of Jesus 'thrice before the cock crew'.

And if you are going to have a cock on top of the steeple of the church, the highest point in most villages of the time, why not make it do some work, as well as being a symbol, by allowing it to rotate and act as a weather-vane?

As the study of the weather became more scientific, in the seventeenth century Robert Hooke, one of the founders of the Royal Society, invented a weather clock. Driven by an ordinary clock, it made pencil recordings of the pressure and wind direction (from a weather-vane mechanically connected to the system) on a rotating sheet of paper – the forerunner of the modern automatic weather station.

Hooke's weather clock was, unfortunately, ahead of its time and often broke down. But it is mentioned in John Evelyn's diary for 19 June 1679 as 'describing the winds, Weather & severall other curious motions, by night and day.'

Bits of equipment that we take for granted have to be invented, like Hooke's device, by people, and even the humble barometer has a proud pedigree by association.

Galileo Galilei puzzled over why the simple suction pumps of his day couldn't lift water more than 34 feet at a time. He thought that the water was being lifted by the suction of the vacuum above the water column.

In 1641, shortly before Galileo died, he passed the problem on to his assistant, Evangelista Torricelli. As Galileo's successor as Court Philosopher in Tuscany, Torricelli tested whether heavier liquids might be 'lifted' over shorter distances by the vacuum.

Experimenting with sea water, honey and mercury (among others), in 1644 he ended up with a three-foot-long glass tube, closed at one end, that could hold a column of mercury. With the tube full and one end sealed with a finger, the tube was stood in a bowl of mercury, closed end uppermost, and unsealed; the mercury column fell down the tube until it was 30 inches high, leaving a vacuum above it. It was the first barometer.

By making tubes with different-sized bulbs on the end, Torricelli showed that the column is actually lifted by the pressure of air pushing down on the mercury in the dish, not by the vacuum above sucking upward. No matter how much (or how little) vacuum there was, the height of the column was the same.

But the key test confirming this idea had still to be carried out. If Torricelli was right, carrying the barometer up a mountain should result in a lowering of the column, since there would be less weight of air pressing down on the mercury in the bowl. The scientist who organised this ultimate test was Blaise Pascal, the French philosopher and mathematical genius.

Pascal could not make the test himself. He was chronically ill and was scared of heights, but in 1648 he sent the materials and instructions to his brother-in-law, Florin Périer, who lived in the Auvergne.

Périer duly carried out the test, accompanied by distinguished clerics and laymen from his town, Clermont-Ferrand. A series of measurements in the town gave a reading of 28 inches, while those on top of the 4,888 foot Puy-de-Dôme gave 24 inches. As well as the barometer, they had invented the altimeter.

*In the days before specialisation, scientists
used to turn their minds to a breathtaking
variety of topics, throwing up some strange
juxtapositions.*

What is the connection between the flight of a cannonball
and the aurora borealis? Both were studied in the seventeenth century by Pierre Gassendi, one of those pioneering
Renaissance men who, in the centuries before science
became compartmentalised, managed to stretch their intel-
lects to cover an astonishing range of what now seem to
be separate – even disparate – disciplines.

Gassendi was born in France in 1592, became a doctor
of theology in 1616 and was ordained in 1617. Alongside
his religious duties he became a professor of mathematics,
an active observational astronomer and a keen sky
watcher. It was this meteorological side of his interests
that led to studies of the aurora borealis, which he gave
the name in 1621. At that time, these lights in the sky
were thought to be a weather phenomenon; they were not
explained in terms of the interaction of charged particles
from the Sun with the Earth's magnetic field until the
present century.

Gassendi's most important scientific experiment took
place in 1640, two years before the birth of Isaac Newton,
when he borrowed a galley from the French navy. The
galley, rowed by slaves, was the fastest means of smooth
transport available at the time. With the slaves rowing flat
out and the ship progressing at top speed across the calm
surface of the Mediterranean, Gassendi dropped a series
of balls from the mast of the moving ship.

As he had expected, but contrary to the common sense
of the day, the balls hit the deck at the foot of the mast
and were not left behind by the ship's motion. This was
one of the first proofs that motion is relative; to the falling

ball, what matters is the 'frame of reference' of the ship, and the ball falls straight down relative to the mast, whatever the speed of the ship.

The same science, running counter to what many people still see as common sense, tells us that if a bullet is fired horizontally from a rifle by a standing marksman at the same moment that another bullet is dropped from shoulder height, both bullets hit the ground simultaneously. The downward motion is independent of the horizontal motion. Which, of course, is why it is possible to juggle successfully while riding a unicycle.

High humidity is good for plants but makes life sticky and uncomfortable for humans, especially for athletes, because the higher the humidity the more difficult it is for your body to keep cool. When preparing to compete in areas of high humidity, athletes sometimes train inside a greenhouse because with practice bodies can become more efficient at handling the effects of moisture-laden air.

Over the years types of hygrometer – instruments designed to measure humidity – have varied entertainingly. Erasmus Darwin (grandfather of Charles) reported a splendid automaton devised by a Mr Edgeworth that moved forward according to the level of moisture in the surrounding air. Mr Edgeworth's automaton consisted of a long strip of wood cut crosswise to the grain and fitted with two backward-facing points at each end. When the air was humid the wood expanded slightly, pushing it forwards. The strip shrank in dry air, causing the tail-end to drag. The wood-strip 'creature' continually went forward propelled by rises and falls in humidity, and the distance it passed 'gave a rough indication of the comparative moisture of the air'.

The amount of water vapour in the air is also responsible for the working of simple weather houses. A twisted hair inside the weather house stretches when it is wet and contracts when it is dry. It is this stretching and shrinking that causes the turntable, on which the man and woman stand, to swivel. The wet-weather man emerges when there is a lot of water in the atmosphere, because humidity stretches the hair allowing the turntable to turn and popping him outside. On a dry day the hair shrinks, pulling the turntable so that the woman takes his place.

These two simple hygrometers are by far the most fun, but the earliest known hygrometer, devised by the Greeks, wins hands down for simplicity. Take a natural sponge and weigh it on a very dry day. Then weigh it every day thereafter. The heavier it is, the more humidity there is in the air. Simple.

It wasn't just scientists who changed the way we think about the weather.

What better, in the heat of summer, than to dream of a white Christmas, with a blazing log fire and a robin perched on a snow-covered bough? But where does our idea that Christmases 'ought' to be white come from? When did you last experience a white Christmas in the Home Counties of England, where the image seems to have such a strong grip?

Perhaps it is precisely because white Christmases are rare that we cherish the image so much. Or perhaps the blame can be laid at the door of one man, Charles Dickens.

The weather in southern England certainly isn't constant from year to year, and minor climatic changes have rippled through history, even before people started worrying about the greenhouse effect. The latest climatic change was the 'Little Ice Age' that was at its height in the seventeenth century but persisted into the nineteenth century.

Born in 1812, Dickens spent the first years of his life at the tag-end of the last phase of the final cold spell of the Little Ice Age. In the first nine years of his life, there were six white Christmases in London, either because snow had fallen or because of heavy frost. In the winter of 1813–14, the Thames at London froze hard enough to walk across, and tented booths offering a variety of entertainments were set up on the ice. The cold winters made a deep impression on the boy, who grew up to write stories that contain the definitive descriptions of traditional white Christmases in southern England.

Before those stories got into print, however, white Christmases in London were a rarity, and today they are almost entirely a thing of the past. But Dickens gave the Victorians their picture of what Christmas 'ought' to be like, and that picture is preserved on every Christmas card that carries the image of a coach-and-four hastening through the snow. Our Christmas cards owe more to Dickens's boyhood, and the last gasp of the Little Ice Age, than to the real weather patterns of the past 150 years.

The winters that made such an impression on Dickens went hand-in-hand with some pretty lousy summer weather, which has left another curious stamp on English literature.

What possessed a nice young girl such as Mary Shelley to write a horrific story like *Frankenstein, or The Modern Prometheus*? A lot of the blame can be attached to the weather in 1816; and some of the blame for the bad weather that summer can be attached to the volcano Tambora, which blew its top in Indonesia a year earlier, sending such a burden of pollution into the atmosphere that it acted as a sunshield and cooled the entire globe over the next few years.

The year 1816 was busy for Mary, who was the daughter of Mary Wollstonecraft and the philosopher William Godwin. Two years earlier, at the age of sixteen, she had met and fallen in love with Percy Bysshe Shelley, and the couple eloped to the continent in July 1814, leaving behind Shelley's pregnant wife, Harriet. In 1815, on the death of his grandfather, Shelley inherited enough money to pay his debts and give him a moderate income, and the couple settled happily in England where Mary gave birth to their first son in January 1816.

In August, the couple, accompanied by Godwin's step-daughter Claire, were supposed to be enjoying the summer weather in a cottage on the shores of Lake Geneva, Switzerland. There, they were close neighbours of the exiled Lord Byron. The weather was so dreadful that the party had to make their own indoor amusements. Among other things this led to Claire becoming pregnant by Byron and giving birth to a daughter in 1817.

One of the seemingly more innocuous indoor activities suggested by Byron was that each member of the party should write a ghost story for the entertainment of the others. Nothing much came of the other efforts, but Mary came up with *Frankenstein*.

It still wasn't quite the end of Mary's interesting year. In December, Shelley's wife Harriet committed suicide by drowning. He married Mary in London on 30 December. They lived not entirely happily, and not quite ever after (Shelley was drowned in 1822).

Not just literature but art came under the influence of weather patterns influenced by nineteenth-century volcanism; and volcanic eruptions still have an influence on the weather today.

During the early years of the 1990s, weather permitting, many parts of Britain were treated to spectacular sunsets, with the deep red of the setting Sun blazing across the horizon while a paler shading of rainbow colours painted pastel stripes across the sky. It looked, as many people commented, like something in a painting by J. M. W. Turner. And that is no coincidence, because Turner's famously colourful paintings of sunsets, once thought to be coloured as much by his imagination as by real life, are now known to be more representational than impressionistic and to owe their origins to the same cause as our own recent display of 'Turneresque' sunsets – volcanic eruptions.

The redness of sunset is caused by dust in the atmosphere. Blue light, which has a shorter wavelength than red light, is more easily scattered by tiny particles of dust or fine droplets of liquid suspended in the stratosphere. So the blue is 'scattered out' of the sunlight, leaving red behind.

Turner's sunsets have been put in perspective by Hubert Lamb of the University of East Anglia. He points out that after a lull in volcanic activity between about 1783 and 1802 there was a series of eruptions that threw dust into the air and produced spectacular optical effects that were commented on by many observers in the first half of the nineteenth century. The famous sunset colours of Turner's work became noticeable after 1807 and prominent in the 1830s, when the stratosphere was most burdened with volcanic debris.

The modern counterparts of those colours can be linked directly with the massive eruption of Mount Pinatubo in June 1991. The bad news is that as well as providing spectacular sunsets, the volcanic debris acts like a sunshield, stopping some of the heat from the Sun from reaching the ground. We seem to have escaped anything quite as bad as the lack of summer in 1816, but who knows when the next spectacular volcano will blow its top?

*The nineteenth century was also the time
when scientists began to be aware of the
broader sweep of changes going on in the
atmospheric environment, although the
scientists involved did not always have a
conventional background in the subject.*

Not many janitors are elected to be Fellows of the Royal
Society; indeed, James Croll, the Scot who pioneered the
modern understanding of Ice Ages, may have been the only
one.

Croll was born in 1821 and spent the early part of his
life in a Scottish village. At the age of thirteen he left school
to work the family croft but read widely and by the age
of sixteen, as he later recalled in his book *Climate and
Time*, he had a 'pretty tolerable' knowledge of the basics
of 'pneumatics, hydrostatics, light, heat, electricity and
magnetism'. He became a millwright, thinking that the
mechanics of the work would be interesting, but found that
'the strong natural tendency of my mind towards abstract
thinking somehow unsuited me for the practical details of
daily work'.

At twenty-one, Croll gave up the job and took up the
study of algebra while working as a carpenter, then marry-
ing and running a tea-shop. The business failed, at least
partly because of his obsession with the wrong kind of
books. He also failed as a hotelier. It is an indication of
his lack of business acumen that he chose to run a hotel
in a Scottish town that already had sixteen inns serving a
community of 3,400 people and that, a teetotaller himself,
he refused to serve whisky to his customers. Among a
succession of fill-in jobs he even worked in the classic one
of insurance salesman before, in 1859, finding his true
niche in the world as a janitor at the Andersonian College
and Museum in Glasgow.

'I have never,' he wrote, 'been in a place so congenial to me.' The pay was poor, and the work menial, but it gave Croll the two things he prized most: time to think and access to a first-rate scientific library. He began to publish scientific papers (one wonders whether the editors of the learned journals realised that the address on the papers was that of the *janitor* of the museum) and in 1864 attracted attention for his work on the theory of Ice Ages.

By 1867, Croll had a post with the Geological Survey of Scotland; in 1876 he was elected a Fellow of the Royal Society. And his Ice Age theory, involving variations in the orbit of the Earth that change the balance of solar heating across the seasons, is still the foundation of modern thinking on the subject.

Scientists are taught to be objective, to analyse the facts and to discard any theory that does not match the facts. Being human, all too many scientists quickly forget this and spend their lives trying to bend the facts to fit their treasured theories. There are a few noble exceptions, one of whom (eventually) persuaded nineteenth-century geologists that there really had been at least one great Ice Age.

The suggestion that the world had once been covered in ice originally came from Jean de Charpentier, a mining engineer working in Switzerland in the first half of the nineteenth century. Impressed by the power of glaciers, he reasoned that great boulders found far away down the Rhône valley must have been carried there by huge prehistoric ice flows.

The suggestion, made in 1834 to a meeting of the Swiss Society of Natural Sciences, infuriated Louis Agassiz, the twenty-seven-year-old Professor of Natural History at the University of Neuchâtel and an expert on fossil fishes. He was sure that glaciers could not move far enough or fast enough to do the trick, and he set out to prove his case.

To this end, he set up an observing station in a hut on the Aar glacier and carefully measured the movement of stakes driven into the ice. Confounded by the discovery that the ice moved much faster than he had thought, and persuaded that it could carry large boulders over long distances, he was converted from critic to believer and became an enthusiastic evangelist for his new beliefs.

He started, in 1837, by dragging reluctant fellow members of the Society of Natural Sciences out of the lecture room and into the mountains to see the evidence for themselves (the task was made easier by the fact that Agassiz was now President of the Society); he continued, in 1840, by publishing a wide-ranging theory of a world covered in ice and ended up by infuriating de Charpentier for the way he had picked up the Ice Age ball and run off with it.

In 1846, Agassiz visited the United States in his quest to study glacial activity. He stayed on at Harvard University, and there became the leading opponent in the USA of Darwin's theory of natural selection, showing that nobody is perfect.

One Victorian scientist who did follow a more conventional career pattern was also one of the first to offer a plausible explanation of why climate changes.

John Tyndall was one of a band of Victorian physicists who changed the way people viewed the world. He is not ranked quite so highly as James Clerk Maxwell, Lord Kelvin or Michael Faraday, but among other things he explained why sunsets are red and was the first to make a connection between changes in the carbon dioxide content of the atmosphere and climate change.

Born in Carlow, Ireland, in 1820, Tyndall worked as a teacher in Hampshire before attending the University of Marburg, Germany, graduating in 1850. He was appointed Professor of Natural Philosophy at the Royal Institution in 1853, and succeeded Faraday as Director of that institution in 1867.

Among his many interests, Tyndall studied the transmission of radiant heat (what we now call infrared radiation) through gases. He measured the absorption of infrared by carbon dioxide and water vapour, and published a paper in 1863 about the effects of greenhouse gases on climate. He was the first person to suggest that Ice Ages occur during periods when the amount of carbon dioxide in the atmosphere is reduced, weakening the greenhouse effect.

Although this is not the primary cause of Ice Ages, recent studies have shown that a reduction in carbon dioxide concentrations does indeed play a part in sustaining Ice Ages.

Tyndall was also interested in the properties of light, and gave a series of lectures in the United States, then a scientific backwater, explaining the latest European ideas. The proceeds were donated to a trust set up to benefit American science.

In 1869 Tyndall found that light passes invisibly through a clear liquid but that the beam is visible when particles are suspended in the liquid, because the light is scattered sideways. He inferred that dust suspended in the air scatters blue light from the setting Sun, leaving red and orange light behind; he went on to show that minute dust particles in the air carry bacteria which are a source of infection.

As if this were not enough for one man, he also helped to set up the scientific journal, *Nature*. Not bad for a Victorian scientist of the second rank!

*None of these speculations are worth a fig
without data, and we owe our understanding
of how the weather and climate have changed
since the nineteenth century in no small
measure to the bright idea of one man, who
also has a literary connection.*

How can meteorologists be sure that observers at weather
stations across the country – or around the world – are
making accurate measurements of conditions around
them? Accurate weather forecasting relies on every weather
station taking accurate measurements under controlled
conditions, and the person who set the standards that are
still in use today was a Scottish lighthouse engineer called
Thomas Stevenson, the father of Robert Louis Stevenson.

Before the Royal Meteorological Society was founded
in 1850, it had been thought that shade temperatures were
reasonably comparable if they were always taken on a
north-facing wall. Meteorological *laissez-faire* was such in
the eighteenth century that temperature was commonly
recorded inside in an unheated room – convenient for
observers who didn't fancy going out in the wind and rain,
but enough to make a modern meteorologist blench.

The Royal Meteorological Society encouraged record-
keeping under standard conditions. To do this, temperatures needed to be recorded from thermometers protected
from the direct heat of the Sun but without being chilled
by direct shade. During the 1870s a series of temperature
monitoring stations was set up all over Britain using the
newly invented Stevenson screen that enabled air temperature to be recorded accurately.

Weather stations today still use Stevenson screens, but
few people who use them know the connection between
this rather mundane piece of meteorological equipment
and the author of *Treasure Island*. Stevenson screens are

boxes, usually painted white, made of louvred panels. The boxes contain wet and dry bulb thermometers, to record both humidity and air temperature. The screen shades instruments from the Sun's direct heat, while the louvred sides allow air to circulate throughout the box. This ensures that the thermometers inside the box are recording the true temperature of the air. The slats on the box floor protect against radiation from the ground.

All Stevenson screens are 1.2 metres above the ground and built to a standardised design so that records from them can be compared accurately. Just the right height, in fact, to double as a cage for Long John Silver's parrot.

Even with data, it may not be possible to work out just what is going on in the atmosphere in time for the information to be useful.

Lewis Fry Richardson was a man ahead of his time. Born in 1881, by 1914 he was superintendent of the meteorological observatory at Eskdalemuir, Scotland, and was keenly interested in the application of mathematics to the inexact art of weather forecasting. It was Richardson's dream to develop a set of equations describing weather systems (a mathematical model) with sufficient accuracy to be able to predict tomorrow's weather from the weather patterns existing today.

Work on that dream was interrupted by the outbreak of the First World War. Richardson was a Quaker and served on the Western Front in the ambulance corps, working on his theory whenever he got the chance. An early draft of his manuscript, which would later be turned into a ground-breaking book, was lost during a battle in 1917 but turned up several months later under a heap of coal and was eventually reunited with its author.

The epic work, *Weather Prediction by Numerical Process*, was finally published in 1922 and described a mathematical technique for forecasting the weather that was, up to a point, successful. The snag was that it generally took Richardson about three months of laborious calculation to produce a weather forecast for the following day – that is, three months in the past by the time the forecast was ready.

Nevertheless, the forecasts were reasonably accurate. All that was needed to make them useful was a way to speed up the calculations. Richardson had the answer. He calculated that an army of 64,000 mathematicians, each equipped with a manual calculating machine, could each be given one small piece of the problem, and together they would be able to make predictions one jump ahead of changes in the real weather.

Unfortunately, Richardson's far-sighted plan to alleviate the unemployment of the 1920s never received funding, and useful numerical forecasting had to await the development of the electronic computer. He died in 1953, just failing to see his ideas put to practical use. But those electronic number crunchers that now give us accurate forecasts three days in advance are all based on the same mathematical principles that Richardson worked out during his moments of calm on the Western Front in the First World War.

4 WHERE THE WIND BLOWS

*Richardson's problem was that he had the
data needed to make an accurate weather
forecast but he lacked the computer power
(human or electronic!) to do the job quickly
enough to be useful. A century before his
time, there was another problem: it was
impossible to gather the data in one place
quickly enough to make forecasting
practicable.*

The key invention in the science of weather forecasting
was the electric telegraph. Before Samuel Morse came up
with a workable system for rapid communications in the
1840s, weather watchers had long been able to take
measurements of temperature and pressure using standardised instruments at different locations, gather them
together and produce a 'synoptic' picture of the weather
over a wide area, from which a forecast could be made.

But when the gathering together had to be done on horse-back (or at best by carrier pigeon) the effort would have been fruitless, since by the time the forecast could be made, it would already be out of date.

And yet, even though those pre-1840s measurements of weather variables are now even more out of date and use-less for forecasting purposes, they have become a mine of information for historians and climatologists interested in 'backcasting', finding out what the weather was like on particular dates, and in particular decades, throughout recent history.

The records come from official weather observatories established in Britain and France in the eighteenth century, from ships' logs, private journals and the chain of observ-ing stations set up by Elector Karl Theodor of the Rhine-land, which spread eastward to Russia. Usable information going back to at least 1780 and covering much of Europe and the North Atlantic has enabled researchers at the Uni-versity of East Anglia to reconstruct the daily weather charts for several specific days of historical interest for special commissions. On the day of the storming of the Bastille, for example, the weather in Paris was 'fine and dry, well suited to outdoor activity', according to climatol-ogist John Kington.

The UEA team has reconstructed daily weather charts for much of the 1780s, as a pilot project, and the available records would allow reconstructions for almost any date since then, if funding were available. This could be of great practical importance if, for example, the backcasters could pick out from the records of the past two centuries a sequence of weather similar to the drought that affected much of Europe in 1995 and use the old records to decide whether the recent drought is 'just one of those things' that has happened before and will happen again naturally or whether it is a sign of a shift in climate caused by human activities.

Once Samuel Morse had established a workable rapid

communications system in the 1840s, it was only a matter of time before telegraphy was used in weather forecasting. By the middle of the 1840s, meteorological observations from far and wide were being gathered in over the wires both in the United States and Europe, and in 1847 Joseph Henry, Secretary of the Smithsonian Institution, proposed a network of telegraphic links to give warning to citizens in the eastern states of storms approaching from the west.

By 1849, more than 200 widely scattered observing stations were reporting to the Smithsonian in Washington, where weather information was displayed for the public on a large map. Daily reports (though not forecasts) were also published in the *Washington Evening Post*, until the system was disrupted by the American Civil War.

In London, the *Daily News* commissioned James Glaisher to collect weather data from a network of observing stations around Britain and published its first 'Daily Weather Report' on 31 August 1848. By 1851, Glaisher was producing daily weather charts, which although not published in the *Daily News*, appeared on display for the edification of visitors at the Great Exhibition.

The great leap forward for forecasting came when disaster, in the form of an unexpected storm, struck the Anglo-French fleet off Balaclava on 14 November 1854, during the Crimean War. Urbain le Verrier of the Paris Observatory later found from the weather records kept at different observing sites that the storm had travelled eastward across Europe. A telegraphic service was promptly set up to collate weather data quickly and ensure that if anything similar happened again, the east would get fair warning of what was on the way. Le Verrier also introduced the system of isobars: lines drawn on a weather map to link places of equal pressure – the barometric equivalent to contour lines.

In Britain, following the Balaclava storm, Vice-Admiral Robert FitzRoy (Charles Darwin's former captain on the voyage of the *Beagle*) was appointed to head the new Meteorological Department of the Board of Trade, the first official meteorological post in the United Kingdom. These measures were a complete success, and since 1854 no Anglo-French fleet has ever been caught in an unexpected storm off the Crimea.

The development of meteorology owes much to the man whose captaincy of HMS *Beagle* helped Charles Darwin to formulate *On the Origin of Species*. Robert FitzRoy learnt the inestimable value of keeping accurate records on the *Beagle*. After the voyage he was appointed Governor of New Zealand, where his spirited defence of the rights of the Maori people annoyed the British colonists so much that they forced his resignation and sent him back to England.

On his return he was made a vice-admiral and joined the Board of Trade as head of the newly created Meteorological Department. The need to predict weather had long been recognised by sailors. FitzRoy's department produced the first daily weather report in 1860. Using the new invention of electric telegraphy they collated weather observations from European stations to prepare three-day weather forecasts, essentially based on knowing what the weather was like in the direction the wind was coming from. Later, in July 1861, weather forecasts were released to the press. These freely available public weather forecasts were vehemently criticised by the Royal Society, who questioned the accuracy of the system used to work them out – not altogether unreasonably since, of course, that system took little account of how weather systems evolved.

FitzRoy had other problems on his mind, however. As a deeply entrenched fundamentalist, he had been devastated by the publication of Darwin's views on evolution. These stresses finally broke his health, and on 30 April 1865 FitzRoy, first head of what became the Met Office and a truly remarkable man, cut his own throat.

*You don't need a network of weather stations,
the electric telegraph and an electronic
computer to be able to work out which way
the wind blows and use that information to
get a rough idea of the local pattern of
weather.*

One of the most useful titbits of practical weather lore is
the rule that if you stand with your back to the wind, then
(in the northern hemisphere) you will have high pressure
on your right and low pressure on your left. In the southern
hemisphere, the pattern is reversed.

Many people know the law, and some of them know
that it is 'Buys Ballot's Law'. But who was Buys Ballot,
and why do the winds blow that way?

The law is named after one Christophorus Henricus
Didericus Buys Ballot, a meteorologist, of Utrecht. He
stated the law in 1857, having based it upon the empirical
observation that the wind blows at right angles to the
pressure gradient in the atmosphere, but without knowing
why this should be so.

The 'why' was worked out by a contemporary of Buys
Ballot, the American William Ferrel, although neither of
them knew of the other's work at first, and they reached
the rule independently. It all has to do with the rotation
of the Earth, which carries every point on the surface round
in a circle once every twenty-four hours.

Near the North Pole, this corresponds to rather leisurely
speeds. At the equator, however, anything on the surface
of the Earth is travelling round at 1,050 miles per hour
while at 60°N the speed is about 500 mph. Air that moves
north from the equator towards the poles carries with it
a memory of the sideways speed it started out with. It is
moving from west to east faster than the Earth's surface
at higher latitudes, and from the point of view of anyone

on the surface the wind seems to be deflected sideways (eastward) by the Coriolis force.

Similarly, air moving south in the northern hemisphere lags behind the surface speed at its new latitudes, and seems to be pushed westward.

When air tries to move from a region of high pressure to a region of low pressure, the Coriolis force comes into play. There is no problem with east–west windflow, but any winds moving north–south are deflected and wound up by the force in such a way that winds blow anticlockwise around low-pressure systems in the northern hemisphere and clockwise around low-pressure systems in the southern hemisphere. The winds tend to blow in circles, obeying Buys Ballot's Law and flowing more or less along the isobars (lines of equal pressure) on a weather map, all of which should make it straightforward to make your own forecast from the chart provided on TV or in your daily paper. But where did the idea for these charts come from?

Francis Galton, a cousin of Charles Darwin, is best remembered today for his ideas on eugenics: especially the belief that human intellectual abilities are inherited. It is less well known that among his 200-odd scientific papers was one reporting a statistical investigation of the efficacy of prayer, and outside of specialist circles nobody now recalls his contributions to meteorology, which may be his most important practical scientific legacy.

Galton's interest in the weather stemmed from the most practical of considerations. He lived from 1822 to 1911, and in the mid-nineteenth century he was interested in finding ways of using weather information to enable sailing ships to pick routes that would minimise the time spent on their voyages.

In 1861, Galton published some of the first meteorological charts, using his own system of symbols to denote the weather in different parts of Britain on 16 January and other selected days that year. He refined the use of 'contour

lines' to join points of equal barometric pressure on a
weather map, and gave those lines the name still used
today, 'isobars'.

This technique of plotting pressure gave us the daily
weather maps so familiar today. It also immediately led
Galton to an important discovery. Meteorologists at the
time already knew that the winds in the northern hemisphere blow anticlockwise around centres of low pressure,
called cyclones; Galton discovered that the winds blow
clockwise around calm regions of high pressure, and, in a
paper published in 1863, he gave those high-pressure
regions the name 'anticyclones'.

This was far from being the limit of Galton's inspiration.
One of his other long-forgotten ideas concerned the possibility of extracting energy from the motion of the waves.
He got the idea from noticing the way in which a small
boat alongside a large vessel is tossed about in rough seas,
and calculated how to turn this energy into useful work
using a system of levers attached to a buoy. All this was
detailed in his notebooks in the early 1870s but never put
to practical use. As a prescient biographer commented not
long after Galton's death, however, 'as our coal and oil
supplies run short, possibly men will turn again to Galton's
suggestion of harnessing the waves'.

*The kind of insights that come from the work
of such pioneers as FitzRoy and Galton help
to put newsworthy weather events in
perspective and give an insight into why
different parts of the world can experience
seemingly paradoxical weather patterns.*

In January 1993 the bottom fell out of the barometers in
the Scottish islands, as the pressure dropped to just 916
millibars at the centre of a storm. Just how low was that,

compared with the normal range of pressures, and how can we put it in perspective?

Because of the way meteorologists define their units of pressure, the average pressure at sea level is, rather curiously, 1,013 mbar (not 1,000 mbar, or 1 bar, as you might expect). The normal range of pressure in Britain is from 940 mbar in the deepest depressions (cyclonic storms) to about 1,050 mbar in the strongest high-pressure systems or anticyclones.

Cyclonic storms are literally regions where the pressure of the air is, ultimately as a result of convection, lower than its surroundings. In an attempt to equalise pressure, winds blow from regions of high pressure to regions of low pressure, but because of the rotation of the Earth the winds are deflected sideways and spiral into the centre of a low in exactly the same way that water spirals down the plug-hole of a bath, except that the winds spiral inward and *upward*.

The spiralling winds blow more strongly when the pressure difference from the outside to the inside of the system is greater. So the lower the pressure in the eye of the storm, the stronger the winds – as Shetland discovered in 1993.

Winds are not the only consequence of the low pressure. Over the sea, the low-pressure region acts like a huge vacuum cleaner, or a giant straw, sucking on the water below and lifting it up. At the same time, the winds may be pushing water towards the land. The result, if a storm coincides with high tide, can be a 'storm surge', sending a wall of water far above the normal high tide and over the coastal defences.

Some forty years ago, in January 1953, a combination of low pressure, winds and high tide sent the sea bursting through the coastal defences of the east of England, flooding 156,000 acres of land and causing the loss of 307 lives.

Even this is small beer by tropical standards. In 1973, the pressure measured in record-breaking typhoon Nora in the western Pacific fell to 877 mbar. Wind speeds reached more than 170 miles an hour. Storms of such severity feed off warm tropical water and cannot occur in British latitudes.

Summer visitors to San Francisco, lightly clad in anticipation of California sunshine, are often surprised, and chilled, to discover the city shrouded in clammy fog. Heading out of the bay area to the splendid beaches not far to the north, they may very well be able to bask in the sunlight, but anyone tempted to take a dip in the Pacific Ocean will soon find that it is uncomfortably cold.

The coldness of that Pacific water is the key to the fogs of San Francisco Bay. The circulation system of the world's oceans is driven by cold water sinking down at high latitudes and circulating as deep currents until, inevitably, it is pushed to the surface by the pressure of more cold water coming along behind.

At the surface, the water warms and returns to high latitudes to complete the cycle. The circulation pattern is rather like the circulation of the atmosphere, but upside down; in both cases, what matters is that it is the surface of the Earth (the top of the ocean but the bottom of the atmosphere) that is warmest.

What matters to would-be sunbathers in San Francisco is that one of the regions of upwelling cold water is off the west coast of the American continent. In summer at the latitude of San Francisco, warm, moist air from the south blows in over the cold ocean currents. As the air cools, the moisture in it condenses to make fog, which can fill the nearly landlocked bay of San Francisco.

As the wind blows inland it warms and the fog thins rapidly. Not far inland from San Francisco, across the Sierra Nevada mountains, there are hot deserts that scarcely ever experience fog.

Along the coast the fogs are common, and 'proper' rainfall is relatively sparse, so the vegetation has adapted to catch as much moisture from the fog as it can. The famous California redwoods catch condensing moisture on their needles, which then drip the water downwards on to the forest floor. The tops of the trees turn fog into rain to feed their roots.

Just the opposite effect, heat carried by a warm ocean current, is responsible for the mildness of the British climate.

'Everybody knows' that the Gulf Stream is responsible for the relatively warm weather experienced in Britain, but just how much does this oceanic 'river' heat our islands and how reliable is it?

The best comparison is to look at the weather experienced at similar latitudes in other parts of the world. Labrador, for example, lies more or less at the same distance from the equator as Newcastle upon Tyne does. And that is the same distance from the equator as the tip of South America.

The water that keeps us warm originates in the Caribbean, flows around the Gulf of Mexico while soaking up heat from the Sun and out past Florida up the coast of North America, then swings across the Atlantic Ocean to wash our shores. In the north-eastern Atlantic, the warm water of the current radiates heat at a rate of a billion megawatts, equivalent to one thousand billion one-bar electric fires floating on the surface and warming the atmosphere.

This heat output is equivalent to the energy obtained from a million large power stations, and keeps northwestern Europe about 6°C warmer than it would otherwise be. The price paid by the ocean current is that it cools and sinks deep below the surface of the sea as it moves southward down the eastern side of the ocean basin.

What would happen if the Gulf Stream faded away before reaching the British Isles? Geological studies show that about 12,000 years ago, after the world had started to warm out of the latest Ice Age, there was a sudden cooling that affected the region around the North Atlantic. The explanation is that melting fresh water from the ice-caps acted as a cold, temporary lid on the salty water of the sea, which made the Gulf Stream give up its heat and sink away southward before reaching Europe.

One of the most predictable consequences of any global warming is that polar ice sheets will melt and spill cold, fresh water into the North Atlantic. Depending on how much water is released, and how soon, one corollary could be that while the world as a whole warms, Britain is given the weather that is really appropriate for its latitude.

It is those westerlies that bring the familiar British rain to these offshore islands, but just how much moisture is there in the air, waiting to fall as rain or snow?

If all the water vapour and all the clouds in the atmosphere could be instantly turned to rain, it would make a layer of water only 25 millimetres (one inch) thick over the entire surface of the globe.

If all that water went into the oceans, the rise in sea level would be just 35 mm, so where does all the rain come from?

One answer is that rainfall is not, of course, distributed evenly around the globe. Some regions (such as England) get more than their share, while others (such as the Sahara Desert) get less, but there is more to the story than this.

Taking the world as a whole, the average rainfall in a single year is about 100 centimetres. In other words, forty

times more rain falls in a single year as there is present in
the atmosphere at any time. This is only possible because
water is evaporating from the oceans and lakes of the
world as fast as it falls as rain, replenishing the humidity
of the air.

Because 100 cm is just forty times 25 mm, this means
that it takes water about nine days (one-fortieth of a year)
to complete the cycle of evaporation and rainfall.

In more everyday units, that annual average global rainfall amounts to 250 million million gallons of water,
which, since the population of Britain is about 55 million,
works out at just over 4.5 million gallons each.

If the temperature of the Earth changes significantly the
amount of water in the air and the amount of rainfall
change accordingly. During the latest Ice Age there was
less evaporation, so the air was drier and there was less
precipitation. If the world warmed by 3°C at the equator,
and the corresponding amount elsewhere, the increase in
evaporation would cause a drop in sea level of about 7 mm
(other things being equal) and would increase the amount
of rain falling around the globe.

Any sailor worth his salt will tell you that a good fall of
rain calms the surface of the sea. Meteorologists have been
trying to account for this, largely unsuccessfully, for well
over a hundred years, but spaceborne radar systems have
now shown that the sailors were right all along, and this
has led to a new theory of how storms leave their footprints
on the water.

The incontrovertible evidence that storms do dampen
the waves in both senses of the word comes from the
SEASAT satellite, which was used to bounce radar waves
off the surface of the ocean. With this particular radar
set-up, the rougher the surface of the sea the stronger the
signal going back to the satellite.

SEASAT's radar showed echo-free regions, dubbed
holes, off the Atlantic coast of North America in exactly

the same places where conventional radar from shore-based stations showed storms to be at work; but the holes were surrounded by rings of increased reflection, corresponding to a squall line.

David Atlas of the Goddard Space Flight Center in Greenbelt, Maryland, explains this as being due to a plume of descending air and heavy rain in the storm, which blows down on to the water, dampening the waves, and spreads out in all directions, producing a squally gust front. But it is definitely the rain in the core of the plume, not the wind, that smooths out the surface of the ocean. Round the edges of the plume, where the rainfall is less intense, the wind actually roughens the surface of the sea.

These features last for about an hour, without moving far across the surface of the sea. The holes are typically a few kilometres across. They seem to be produced when strong winds several kilometres above sea level dip down to touch the surface, but the researchers have no explanation for why the 'impact zone' should stay in more or less the same place for so long.

Old sea dogs will be glad to be vindicated; modern Met men may have to do some further thinking, since their interpretation of global radar studies of this kind is based on the assumption that storms do not affect the radar signal from the sea surface. Well, you can't win them all!

All the weather is held in place in the lowest layer of the atmosphere by an invisible lid, without which our planet would have a very different pattern of winds and climate.

As we saw in the Introduction, there is a 'lid' on the weather layer of the atmosphere, which stops hot air rising much more than 10 kilometres above the ground.

The weather layer of the atmosphere, from the surface

of the Earth up to about 10–15 km (the exact height depends on latitude and the season), is called the troposphere. The way that it gets warm is not by absorbing heat from the Sun directly. Instead, the energy in sunlight passes through the atmosphere almost unobstructed, and warms the surface of the Earth. It is the warm surface of the planet that, in turn, warms the *bottom* of the atmosphere, and sets the hot air in convective motion.

So the average temperature of the air actually falls off with height (moving away from the warm surface of the planet), from about 15°C at the bottom to a chilly –60°C at the boundary between the troposphere and the stratosphere, the tropopause.

In the stratosphere, above about 15 km, temperature increases once again, nearly all the way up to freezing at an altitude of about 50 km. There is no mystery about this. It happens because some solar energy, called ultraviolet radiation, is absorbed by ozone molecules in the stratosphere.

Hot air at the Earth's surface rises by convection, forms clouds and rain, cools, circulates and returns to the surface once again, making the patterns of wind and weather we know. All of this takes place under the lid of the stratosphere, which, being warmer than the top of the troposphere, suppresses convection.

Many people are concerned that destruction of ozone in the stratosphere (a likely result of the release of CFCs and other chemicals by human activities) might allow solar ultraviolet radiation to penetrate to the ground, causing skin cancer and blindness, and damaging crops. There is a less well known but no less important risk that destruction of stratospheric ozone will make the stratosphere cool, weakening the lid on weather systems.

If that happens, convection will penetrate higher into the atmosphere, above 15 km. Clouds will form at higher altitudes than they do now, and weather patterns will change in unpredictable ways. And all this would be happening at a time when more heat is being trapped near the ground, through the greenhouse effect, which would stimulate convection and make the rising air rise more vigorously.

> *Curiously, it is a lid, not what is usually meant by the term 'greenhouse effect', that keeps a greenhouse warm inside.*

What is it that keeps a greenhouse warm? First, a reminder of how the 'greenhouse effect', a misnomer applied in error to something that really ought to be called 'the atmosphere effect', works.

That effect works like this: energy from the Sun, chiefly in the form of visible light, passes almost unimpeded through the atmosphere of the Earth and warms the surface of the land or sea. That warm surface radiates energy outward in its turn, but the wavelength of radiated energy depends on the temperature of the object doing the radiating – that is why a 'white-hot' poker is hotter than a 'red-hot' poker. The surface of the Sun is at a temperature of about 6,000°C, which is why it radiates visible light. The surface of the Earth is at a temperature of about 15°C (averaged over the whole planet) and radiates mainly infrared energy.

Infrared energy is the heat you can feel if you hold your hand near a hot radiator. It has longer wavelengths than visible light and, unlike visible light, it is absorbed by such gases as carbon dioxide and water vapour in the air, which then re-radiate some of the energy back to the surface of the Earth, keeping it warmer than it would be if our planet had no atmosphere.

What goes on inside a greenhouse? Certainly not the greenhouse effect. Experiments have been carried out with miniature greenhouses – boxes with transparent lids made of various substances – left out in the Sun. They show that even when the 'glass' in the greenhouse is actually a substance that allows infrared radiation to escape, the greenhouse warms up very nearly as satisfactorily as a greenhouse made of ordinary glass, which does trap some infrared. The reason is that the glass in a greenhouse acts as a physical barrier on hot air, which warms inside the greenhouse and tries to rise.

This lid on rising warm air is almost entirely responsible for the warmth inside a greenhouse. The lid has to be transparent to visible light to let the Sun's energy in, but it matters scarcely a jot whether or not it is transparent to the infrared which really is trapped by the atmosphere effect to keep the Earth itself warm.

You have to be careful about lids. Some of them are not as effective as you might guess.

Pale-skinned people who are worried about sunburn might think it is safer to do their sunbathing on a cloudy day. They could be wrong, according to researchers who have been making some observations of sunlight at the Mauna Loa Observatory on a Hawaiian mountaintop.

The arduous task undertaken by Forrest M. Mimms, John E. Frederick and their colleagues is to go back to Hawaii every summer, starting in June 1994, to carry out a series of measurements dubbed the Hawaiian Ultraviolet Survey. The serious side of this research is that, apart from causing sunburn, ultraviolet radiation from the Sun can be very damaging to crops, and there are fears that the amount of this radiation reaching the ground may be increasing as human activities lead to a depletion of ozone in the stratosphere high above our heads.

Like ordinary visible sunlight, the peak amount of solar ultraviolet radiation reaching the ground on a cloudless day occurs at noon, when the Sun is most nearly overhead. On cloudy days, as you might expect, the amount of ultraviolet radiation reaching the ground dips sharply whenever a cloud passes overhead. But the researchers found that their instruments, located at various sites on Hawaii, including the top of Mauna Loa, also recorded a dramatic increase in ultraviolet radiation from time to time on days when there were cumulus clouds drifting across the sky.

The explanation for this is that the water droplets that make up the clouds are very good at scattering ultraviolet radiation, so when there is no cloud actually blocking the Sun the amount of this radiation reaching the ground increases, as some ultraviolet comes directly from the Sun as usual and some more arrives indirectly after being scattered off the sides of the clouds.

When the clouds were around at noon, the effect was to increase the total amount of ultraviolet reaching the instruments by as much as a quarter over the maximum amount received when there were no clouds in the sky. 'The general public should be advised,' say the researchers, 'that cumulus clouds near the Sun can significantly intensify solar ultraviolet.'

If you want to avoid sunburn, maybe the best thing to do is stay indoors and watch TV. But there's a snag . . .

A settled spell of fine summer weather usually brings happiness to holidaymakers in the south of England; but they may be baffled to find French TV stations interfering with their favourite programmes. Curiously, both the fine weather and the TV interference are caused by the same phenomenon.

It happens when there is a large, settled area of high

pressure (an anticyclone) in the vicinity. Air sinks within an anticyclone, piling up to make a kind of atmospheric hill, which keeps weather fronts at bay. But the sinking air also gets warm as it is compressed by the weight of air above. This can lead to a temperature inversion, with the air a few thousand feet above the ground warmer than the air at the surface. This is what deflects the TV signals.

Normally, both VHF/FM radio waves and UHF TV signals pass in a straight line through the atmosphere and out into space. You can pick up the signals only if you are in the line of sight from the transmitter; but where there is an inversion, the properties of the atmosphere are changed so that the signals are gently bent over as they enter the layer and end up pointing back down to the ground.

The phenomenon is known as ducting, and it is exactly equivalent to the way a mirage forms when light rays are bent as they pass through layers of air with different temperatures (and therefore different densities) near the surface of the ground.

Although ducting may annoy TV watchers, it brings delight to some radio enthusiasts. VHF stations that are far over the horizon can sometimes be heard loud and clear over distances of hundreds of miles, giving opportunities for a kind of radiophonic stamp-collecting, tuning in to exotic stations. Spanish radio stations can, for example, be heard in the British Midlands when ducting occurs, and the record for long-range ducting spans 2,500 miles between Hawaii and California.

Next time the weather is set fair, try tuning along the dial of your FM radio. You might be surprised at what you hear.

*Settled spells of anticyclonic weather can
bring other problems, in the form of pollution.*

What is the difference between summertime smog and
wintertime smog? Pollution statistics in the UK used to be
given throughout the year for nitrogen dioxide and sulphur
dioxide, but since 1995, in summer, the reports now focus
on ozone and nitrogen dioxide. The reason is that the
different combinations of pollutants pose the worst problems in the different seasons.

In the summertime, the problem that arises during pro-
longed spells of still, sunny weather is that the action of
sunlight on various pollutant gases causes photochemical
reactions that produce ozone. Ozone is a form of oxygen,
but unlike the oxygen that is essential for life, each ozone
molecule contains three atoms instead of two. This seemingly minor difference is enough to make the gas toxic and
unpleasant even in very small doses.

The chemicals involved in the reactions that produce
ozone near the ground include oxides of nitrogen, produced from vehicle exhausts and by burning gas, oil and
coal, as well as hydrocarbons, given off as vapours from
petrol, solvents and industrial processes.

Wintertime smog is different. It occurs when a lid of
cold air called an inversion forms over a city, trapping
pollution near the ground. In wintertime the Sun is too
weak to trigger the reactions that produce ozone, so the
pollutants are essentially those produced by human activities: nitrogen dioxide as before, but also sulphur dioxide
from the combustion of fossil fuels and other compounds.

Severe wintertime smog is less common in cities such as
London than it used to be, thanks to the various Clean
Air Acts; but it can be a killer if another problem affecting
breathing, such as a 'flu epidemic, strikes at the same time.
The moral? Watch the pollution figures, and when they

rise, winter or summer, stay indoors as much as possible. It would also help if you gave up your car.

Away with doom and gloom, at least for the time being. Here's a bit of old-fashioned advice on do-it-yourself forecasting.

Watching the weather has always been the British obsession, and back in 1894 *Enquire Within upon Everything*, a compendium of information and advice that was a hot seller in the bookshops of the time, advised on the simple construction of a home-made chemical barometer. First you take a long, narrow glass bottle and put into it two and a half drachms of camphor and eleven drachms of spirit wine. When the camphor is dissolved, add nine drachms of water, thirty-eight grains of potash and thirty-eight grains of sal ammoniac. Dissolve the lot in the water before mixing with the camphorated spirit and then shake the bottle vigorously. Cork the bottle tightly and make a small hole in the cork using a red hot needle. Now your completed bottle barometer can be hung up or placed in any stationary position. By observing how the different materials change colour with the onset of rainy weather you will soon be able to reach that vital umbrella decision.

Buying the ingredients in Boots might nowadays cause a little difficulty and embarrassment, and the construction of your chemical barometer may put you in some degree of danger – but at least you can resolve the weighty problem of deciding whether to take your umbrella with you.

If constructing a chemical barometer seems a little beyond you, *Enquire Within* also recommends standing outside at night to search the heavens for signs of oncoming rain. If the Moon and stars grow dim and there is a ring around the Moon, get out that umbrella. Daytime is even richer with portent. When the sky is tinged with sea green, rain is due to fall in torrents. When tinged with deep blue it will be showery. If the Sun's rays appear like 'Moses's horns – if white at setting or shorn of his rays, or if he goes down into a bank of clouds in the horizon' bad weather is surely on its way.

And if you fail so miserably at predicting the rain that you go out and get soaked to the skin, *Enquire Within* advises curling up with a bowl of steaming hot onions in milk. That should teach you to try harder next time.

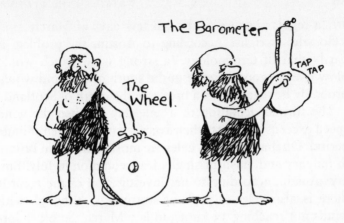

The Barometer

The Wheel.

TAP TAP

5 FROM ONE EXTREME TO ANOTHER

Like the great storm that struck the Anglo-French fleet off the Crimea in 1854, some of the most fascinating features of our weather are extreme events – whether forecast accurately or not.

'Everybody knows' that gales are more common at the time of the equinoxes, late in September and March. But, as Jill Austin of the University of East Anglia has pointed out, it all depends what you mean by a 'gale'.

The experts have certainly had trouble agreeing among themselves. The official *Meteorological Office Glossary* says that the idea of equinoctial gales 'is not supported by observations', and that gales are more common near the time of the winter solstice, around Christmas. But David Bowen's book *Britain's Weather* firmly says that storms are 'a regular feature of the last few days of March'.

So who is right? According to Austin, the problem is partly that of terminology: 'a strong wind which would blow over a wooden fence in the south of England would probably be regarded as a breeze in the north of Scotland.'

The formal definition of a gale day is when the wind speed exceeds 33 knots when averaged over any ten-minute period. On that criterion, gales are most common in Britain in January and, unsurprisingly, least common in July. But, says Austin, according to her investigation of the records there is also a lesser peak of storminess, although with winds not reaching 33 knots, in late March. So older surveys which stuck to the strict definition of a gale day failed to highlight the storms responsible for the folklore about equinoctial gales.

It's all to do with the way that storm tracks move north as the daylight hours increase in early spring. And since the shift of the storm track across Britain can occur in just a few days at the end of March, the effect tends to be obscured in the monthly averages which are a usual way of presenting seasonal weather data.

A blizzard by any other name might still feel as cold; but where does the word come from? Just over a hundred years ago, following a blizzard that swept across the United States in March 1888, a storm of words to rival the blizzard itself raged across the Atlantic, with claim and counterclaim as to the origin of the term.

The storm itself was an epic, raging over the eastern United States from 12 to 14 March, with winds of forty-eight miles an hour recorded in New York City and snowdrifts up to forty feet high. Many babies born at the time were given names such as 'Storm' or 'Tempest', and for years people gathered on the anniversary of the great storm to reminisce about their experiences in the blizzard.

The weather system that brought such havoc to New England travelled across the Atlantic and did the same sort of thing, though on a lesser scale, to Old England and parts of mainland Europe, at which point it became the source of an etymological controversy.

In London, *The Times*, in an article about the storm, suggested that the word 'blizzard' originated from a common dialect expression from the Midlands, 'may I be blizzered', meaning 'may I be bowled over'. The *New York Times* immediately took the Thunderer to task, claiming the word for America, and suggesting that it was 'a bit of onomatopoeia – supposed to sound more or less like the thing it denotes'.

The Germans were having none of that. When the storm, still raging on 19 March 1888, struck their country, the German newspapers referred to it as 'the American blizzard', and said that the word originated from the German 'Blitz', meaning 'lightning'.

How does the word for lightning get attached to a snowstorm? Probably, according to Gary Lockhart's book *The Weather Companion* (1988), thanks to German settlers in the US, describing such storms as blowing up 'blitzartig', meaning 'like lightning'. It's a small step from *blitzartig* to *blizzard*, providing an etymological score draw for the American and German papers, and leaving the Thunderer not so much bowled over as run out without scoring.

Richard Wild of the University of Derby offers a different explanation. According to Wild, the term was in use in the United States in the 1820s, but with a different meaning – a sharp blow or a knock, from which it came to mean a shot. In 1834, Davy Crockett used the word in this way when he wrote of having taken 'a blizzard' at some deer. By 1846 a blizzard was a cannon shot, and during the American Civil War it described a volley of musketry.

In the 1860s, severe American snowstorms were called snow squalls, and the transfer of the name blizzard to them occurred, according to Wild, during a severe storm that struck Iowa in December 1876.

Although the colloquial use of the term did indeed
spread across the Atlantic in the 1880s, the first official
use of the word blizzard by the UK meteorological estab-
lishment was to describe a storm that struck at the end of
February 1937. And it was as recently as 1958 that the
US Weather Service came up with a formal definition of a
blizzard: a cyclonic storm with horizontal wind greater
than 35 mph, enough falling snow to limit visibility to 150
metres and air temperature below minus 7 degrees Celsius.

This is a bit severe for the UK, and since 1991 the Met
Office definition of a blizzard has been a storm of at least
Force 7 with snowfall keeping visibility below 200 metres.
As Wild points out, this doesn't mention the popular image
of blizzards bringing heavy snowfalls that cut off isolated
settlements. He says he would welcome suggestions on
how a blizzard should be redefined to take account of this
popular image.

*Gales and blizzards are fortunately rare, but
even quite common weather phenomena can
take extreme forms.*

In Britain, hail is (usually) no more than an inconvenience.
Globally, though, it can be one of nature's most destructive
forces, and hail insurance in the US amounts to over a
billion dollars a year. We are used to thinking of hailstones
as no bigger than peas, 10–15 mm (up to half an inch) in
diameter; but they have been known to reach the size of
baseballs.

On 14 July 1953, a hailstorm sweeping over Alberta
Province in Canada rained golfball-sized hailstones over a
path 225 km long and 8 km wide, accompanied by winds
of over 120 km per hour. A biologist working with the
US Fish and Wildlife service, Allen Smith, described the
consequences: 'Grasses and herbs were shredded beyond

recognition and beaten into the earth. Trees and shrubs were stripped of all leaves and small branches and the bark on one side of the larger trees had been torn away or deeply gouged by hailstones.'

The lumps of ice that can do such damage start their lives as frozen raindrops which are tossed up and down by the violent vertical air currents, reaching speeds above 30 metres per second, in a cumulo-nimbus storm cloud. On their journeys through the interior of the cloud, the droplets alternately melt and freeze, forming concentric layers of ice that can be seen if you slice through a hailstone.

When the forming hailstone inside a cloud moves into a region of cloud that has a low water content, freezing happens so quickly that air is trapped inside it, producing a layer of white ice. In regions of the cloud with a high water content, freezing time is slower, producing clear ice layers. Layer builds up over layer like an onionskin every time the hailstone bounces up to the freezing top of the cloud and back down again until the hailstone finally falls to the ground. Eventually, the icy 'stone' falls out of the cloud and down to the ground.

An unsigned eyewitness report in *The Times of India* dated 7 May 1888 described the largest hailstones on record. One weighed one and a half pounds, another two pounds and was described as 'the size of an average melon'.

One of the more bizarre features of agricultural life in the former Soviet Union was the provision of anti-aircraft guns to protect the grain prairies from hail. The guns were used to fire shells containing silver iodide crystals into threatening storm clouds, encouraging the formation of many smaller ice crystals, in place of larger hailstones, by providing 'seeds' on which crystals could grow. Considerable success was claimed for the trick, and communes also used a variety of rockets, as well as gunfire, in their war against the weather. But there are no reliable scientific records of the effect of all this on the clouds.

Relaxing in a deckchair in the middle of a May afternoon is a seductive thought, but if past form is anything to go by you could get a freezingly unpleasant surprise, because that is the prime time for hailstorms. One May Day a little over thirty-five years ago, a hailstorm swept over North Crawley in Buckinghamshire dropping hailstones over six inches in diameter, damaging crops and gardens, and no doubt frightening the horses. This event, while extreme, was not unseasonable.

A hailstorm falling on the English army near Paris in the spring of 1360 is reported to have killed hundreds of soldiers and horses, when hailstones the size of goose eggs were said to have hurtled down on the army at great force. Possibly history has made the fall even more extreme than it actually was; but its effect on Edward III, at that point an overwhelming victor in the first phase of what became the Hundred Years War, was so dramatic that he agreed to sign the treaty of Bretigny, giving the exhausted French nine years in which to recover their strength. Arguably, without that hailstorm France would be part of Britain today.

Some claims of extreme weather phenomena have to be taken with a pinch of salt, but not when they come from two policemen, who witnessed the events and took careful notes of what they saw. The *Meteorological Magazine* (a Met Office journal published by HMSO) has dug up just such an eyewitness account of dramatic events that took place on the night of Friday, 18 September 1992 at Foulness, Essex.

At two o'clock in the morning, the lightning was so frequent and intense that it was like daylight. Constable Ian Bailey, out on foot patrol with his dog, described it as 'like staring into the strobe lights at a disco', and, because it was unsettling his dog, he decided to return to his base for a break. It was as well that he did.

As his sergeant described it, by 02.35 the rain was torrential, with a lake of water two inches deep threatening to come through the doors, and at 02.50 the first hailstones began tapping at the windows.

'Suddenly it sounded as though there were a thousand people outside throwing stones at the windows. Visibility was cut to only a matter of about 50 feet and I honestly thought that the windows were going to crash in.' In a few minutes, the road outside was covered with hailstones the size of golfballs.

Both the police Landrover and their private cars were damaged by the hailstones, one with a broken windscreen, and the blue light on the Landrover had been smashed. Two hours later the road was still covered in hailstones, which had not noticeably shrunk.

The storm was extremely localised, but another eyewitness describes how he was woken by the thunder and was standing in his conservatory watching the storm when hailstones started to come straight through the corrugated Perspex roof. Many were a couple of centimetres in diameter; the largest was 'the size of a large chicken egg'.

After the storm, RSPCA inspectors found more than 3,000 birds killed by the hail. One sheep and eight hares were also killed. Some of the hailstones were kept in freezers for later inspection. Their average size was 2.5 cm, with the largest nearly 5 cm long and 4 cm wide, confirming the reliability of the eyewitnesses.

Events that might pass without comment in some parts of the world qualify as extreme phenomena when they occur in unexpected places.

Asked about tornadoes, most people will think of Dorothy's cabin in Kansas whirling away in *The Wizard of Oz*; but just over forty years ago a tornado sent roofs flying across north London.

The world's greatest windspeeds happen inside a tornado. Winds in the whirling funnel of air can whip round at 500 km an hour. Most happen in the US, which experiences about 500 every year. Some measure 100 metres across and move across the ground at 200 km an hour.

The Great Acton Tornado twisted across north-west London at around 5 p.m. on 8 December 1954. The winds in it reached speeds of over 50 km an hour. Not quite up to the most severe American tornadoes, but bad enough to leave a trail of destruction up to 500 metres wide tearing through Brentford, Chiswick, Willesden, Golders Green and Hampstead.

Wind isn't the only wrecking force in a tornado. The pressure inside the rotating funnel is extremely low, hundreds of millibars lower than normal atmospheric pressure. When it passes over a particular spot, be it in Kansas or Acton, there is a sudden and dramatic fall in pressure. When this happens over a building, the pressure inside it is far greater than the pressure outside it. In extreme cases this can cause a building to be totally destroyed, as the pressure inside makes it explode.

The tornado ripping through Chiswick that evening was strong enough to lift roofs off Gunnersbury Station. It also did a grand job of blocking the railway tracks with debris. Rail transport came to a halt and the only route home for commuters was via the road – unfortunately, not paved with yellow bricks.

While Gunnersbury Park was left licking its wounds, Acton was just starting to suffer. Full-grown trees were twisted so fiercely by the tornado's circling wind that they snapped off a few metres from the ground. The end walls of houses were blown out, and roofs were torn off. Many garden sheds were whisked away, never to be seen in quite the same form again; but, thankfully, no tunefully optimistic young girls were reported missing.

Startled inhabitants of East Sussex were equally surprised in 1995 to see the characteristic funnel-shaped clouds of tornadoes near a supermarket on the outskirts of Brighton and in at least three places near the county town of Lewes. Stretching down the clouds, two of the tornado funnels seem to have touched the ground for a short time, but neither did any damage.

Tornadoes form where relatively cool, dry air moves over the top of warm, wet air, when changes in wind speed and direction can create a swirling vortex. This happens frequently in parts of North America, where the cold dry air from the Rockies moves east over warm, wet air moving north from the Gulf of Mexico.

Because the air pressure in the centre of a tornado is so low, it acts like a giant vacuum cleaner sucking up objects from the ground. When the tornado eventually loses energy and collapses, anything it has sucked up will fall back to the ground; this may explain curious falls of small fish, frogs and hay from the sky.

A tornado that touches the surface of the sea sucks water up inside itself to make a waterspout. Seen from a distance, waterspouts look like large sinuous creatures rising from the ocean and are probably the basis of seafarers' legends about sea monsters.

Tornadoes in Britain are much more rare, and less severe, than those in Kansas because the conditions are seldom right to generate them. But late in the summer, with warm air over the sea (which retains summer heat longer than the land does) and the first cold air of autumn moving down from the north, one place where you might expect to find the occasional modest British tornado is over the South Downs. Rare enough to write home about, but not entirely unprecedented in the annals of British weather.

*Changing patterns of warm and cold water
on a larger scale can bring about global
extremes of weather.*

Climatologists have recently discovered that when the temperature of the ocean in the southern hemisphere rises by a couple of degrees Celsius, there is usually a decline in rainfall in the region of Africa known as the Sahel, extending across the continent just south of the Sahara Desert.

This pattern – an example of what the experts call a 'global teleconnection' – is linked to the El Niño phenomenon, in which the western tropical Pacific cools while the eastern tropical Pacific warms. The oceanic changes often begin in December, and their proximity to Christmas led Spanish-speaking South Americans to give the phenomenon the name, which literally means 'the boy' but is a colloquial reference to Jesus Christ. Such events occur every few years and although their exact cause is still unknown, the experts have learned to interpret the early stages of the development of El Niño, and give a few months' warning of its arrival.

The advance warning can be useful, since El Niño disrupts weather conditions around the Pacific. It brings heavy rain and flooding to countries such as Ecuador and Peru in South America, but drought to Australia. One of the most severe El Niños occurred in 1982–3, when bush fires reached the suburbs of Melbourne.

The switch of warm water back to the western Pacific – now known as La Niña, since it was felt that 'anti-El Niño' had overtones of blasphemy – can be just as disruptive. At the end of the 1980s, La Niña was blamed for intense storms that hit Australia and parts of eastern Asia, while this time it was the turn of North America to suffer drought and harvest failures. Floods also hit Bangladesh and Sudan, both regions where El Niño brings drought, as the weather pattern reversed.

Oceanographers and climatologists have been studying the El Niño/La Niña cycle as part of a project called TOGA (Tropical Ocean/Global Atmosphere), and have now linked it to droughts not just around the Pacific but in India and Africa. The change in wind patterns associated with the change in temperature patterns is so great that the repercussions literally ripple around the world, causing the Indian monsoon to fail and, as happened dramatically in the early 1980s, bringing drought to the Sahel.

As the world warms through the greenhouse effect, some climatologists fear that El Niño itself will get stronger, and that the switch from El Niño to La Niña will be more violent, as the Pacific Ocean responds to the human impact on climate. The next time you see pictures of starving Africans on your TV screens, it may be directly as a result of the profligate use of fossil fuels in the rich world.

There are some weather extremes that it is hard to prepare for, even when you have a rough idea of when they are coming.

The Alabama coastline of the United States is due to experience a hurricane bigger than anything in the history of the United States, sometime in the next hundred years. That may not seem like much of a forecast, but in fact it is a triumph of a new analysis that has reconstructed the patterns of past hurricane activity in the Gulf of Mexico region over the past 5,000 years. Since historical weather records for the region go back only 120 years, this means that for the first time meteorologists have a sound statistical basis on which to make their hurricane forecasts.

The trick, used by researchers from Louisiana State University in Baton Rouge, depends on identifying the

'fingerprints' left by ancient hurricanes in the sediments of
a lake near the coast of Alabama. These sediments are laid
down year by year at the bottom of the lake, so a core
drilled through the sediments provides a probe back in
time.

There was a large storm in the region in 1979 (Hurricane
Frederick), which carried sand away from the beaches and
dumped it into Lake Shelby, just inland. By identifying this
layer of sand in the sediments, the Baton Rouge team knew
what kind of traces older hurricanes should have left. And
they were able to date the older sediments accurately, using
the radioactive carbon technique, which is now a standard
tool of archaeologists and geologists.

Although Frederick was a strong storm, it carried sand
only into the part of Lake Shelby nearest to the beach.
Some of the older sediments, however, contain sand that
was blown into the centre of the lake, much further from
the beach. The researchers infer that this can have been
brought about only by much stronger storms, catastrophic
hurricanes more powerful than anything that has struck
in the region since historical records began.

Over the past 5,000 years, the sediments show that such
super-hurricanes have struck Alabama on average every
600 years. The last storm of this nature to strike the region
hit 770 years ago. So the next disastrous hurricane is
already overdue, statistically speaking, and is very likely
to strike within the next hundred years.

6 MYTHS AND LEGENDS

Some of the most fascinating stories about the weather form the basis of myths and legends. They may sound like old wives' tales, but very often there is a grain of truth within them.

If you saw folk wandering in the woods on Maundy Thursday, collecting twigs and taking them home to nail above the door, they may not have been quite as daft as you thought. If you want to protect your house from storms, English folklore strongly recommends that on Maundy Thursday you should cut a piece of hawthorn wood and nail it above the door. This is said to make the house and its inhabitants safe from death by lightning.

The really cautious might also have been seen out on Palm Sunday gathering in some St John's wort, hazel, holly, mistletoe and blasted oak. All are said to be extremely useful anti-lightning charms, especially if gathered on that

auspicious day, and they also make the house look extra
festive at Easter. But, alas, science can offer no comfort
concerning this piece of folklore. With or without magic
twigs, lightning really can injure and kill.

Forked lightning zigzags to the ground at 100 km
per second. One of the safest places to be when that happens is inside a car. If the car is struck by lightning the
steel skin will conduct the electricity to the ground. Sadly,
the bell-ringers of eighteenth-century Germany did not
have this option, and a German text published in 1784
recounted that during the previous thirty-three years 386
church towers had been struck by lightning and 103 bell-
ringers killed during the performance of their duties.

Roy Sullivan, a National Park Ranger in Virginia, USA,
would have done well to have stayed inside his car twenty-
four hours a day. He was struck by lightning seven times
in his life before he died of (non-electrical) natural causes
in 1983. If you are out in a storm never shelter under an
isolated tall tree. Lightning looks for the quickest path to
the ground and could strike it. You would do best to hide
under a hedge or bush. Folk wisdom, of course, worked
this out years ago and developed a handy rhyme to hammer
home the point.

> Beware the oak,
> It draws the stroke.
> Avoid the ash,
> It draws the flash,
> But under the thorn
> You'll come to no harm.

Why are the seasons so complicated? in the northern hemisphere, the 'longest day', when the Sun spends the most
hours above the horizon, is at the end of June. But the
hottest weather comes later, in July and August, when the
evenings and mornings are growing darker, and we receive
less heat from the Sun each day.

The Romans thought they had the answer. They noticed that the star Sirius, the brightest in the night sky, rose highest above the horizon in the weeks from July to mid-August. It seemed obvious to them that Sirius must be giving off heat that warmed the world even when the number of sunlit hours in the day began to decline.

Sirius lies in the constellation Canis Major and is also known as the Dog Star. So the not-so-long hot days of summer became known as the 'dog days', a name now also used, by extension, to apply to any period of inactivity.

Unfortunately, the Romans were completely wrong about why the dog days of summer are so hot. The real reason is that the ground beneath our feet has been soaking up heat ever since the spring (more or less since the time of the equinox in March), and this acts like a reservoir of warmth.

When the solar influence begins to wane, the stored heat from the ground leaks back out into the air, giving us, for a time, a double dose of warmth and making for hot, sleepless nights. That, of course, is why we don't all freeze as soon as the Sun dips below the horizon.

In winter, the reverse effect is at work. All through the autumn, heat is draining out of the ground and it continues to do so for weeks *after* the 'shortest day'. It is only in late February and March that there is enough heat coming in from the Sun to begin to replenish the reservoir.

In Britain, on the edge of an ocean, a related effect helps to ameliorate seasonal extremes. The ocean is an even more ponderous heat store, slow to warm and slow to cool. It is relatively warm in winter, compared to the land, and relatively cool in summer. That is why we do not experience the extreme range of temperatures of continental interiors, such as those of North America and Siberia.

*   *   *

Late August is a time for enjoying the last of the summer Sun, if you are lucky, and time to start planning for the autumn ahead. It is a time pregnant with signs and portents for the coming autumn and winter, many of them linked with weather conditions on St Bartholomew's Day, 24 August. The Shepherd's Calendar cautions that 'if St Bartholomew's Day be misty, the morning beginning with hoar frost, then cold weather will come soon followed by a freezing winter'. A hoar frost at the end of August would be a very nasty shock indeed, especially for gardeners; but folklore also dictates that 'If the 24th of August be fair and clear, Then hope for a prosperous autumn that year . . .'

Why St Bartholomew's Day should be the source of so many weather legends is a mystery. St Bartholomew himself was one of the more unassuming apostles. He was an intrepid traveller in the East but appears to have spent little or no time in Europe. After travelling through India, Ethiopia, Mesopotamia, Parthia and Lycaonia (the last two now in Iran and Turkey), his missions ended when he was finally beaten and beheaded on the orders of Astyages, King of Babylon. During the second century St Pantaenus of Alexandria found the Gospel of St Matthew. This Gospel had been left behind by Bartholomew during his travels to India but little else is known of him. Even though there appears to be no direct link between Bartholomew and weather prediction, legends connecting St Bartholomew's Day with the forthcoming autumn and winter exist all over Europe.

In Rome, if it rains on 24 August, rain is expected for forty days thereafter. Conversely, in Germany if 24 August is fair and clear a prosperous autumn and harvest is anticipated.

Perhaps the belief in the powers of weather forecasting stemming from St Bartholomew's Day comes less from the saint and more from some forgotten pre-Christian festival. Indeed, within the Greek Orthodox Church,

St Bartholomew's Day is celebrated on 11 June and is free of associations with weather lore. Whatever the source, watch closely. As they say in France, 'as Bartholomew's Day then so the whole of autumn comes'.

Most people have heard the story about the weather on St Swithun's Day and feel uneasy if it rains on 15 July in case we are in for forty days and nights of further wet weather. The legend is connected with a story that Swithun, who died in 862, was originally buried outside Winchester Cathedral, because he wanted to be 'exposed to the feet of passers-by and the drops falling from above'. So when Swithun's body was moved to a new tomb within Winchester Cathedral on 15 July 971, he sent a terrible storm in protest.

But Swithun is not the only saint alleged to have an influence on British weather, and they aren't all as mean with the weather they send as Swithun. St Martin is said to grant us three days of warmer weather around his saint's day on 11 November.

This legend of 'St Martin's summer' stems from the story that Martin, who was then Bishop of Tours in France, found a poor man cowering in the November cold near his cathedral. Martin is said to have torn his cloak in two, keeping half for himself and giving the other half to the beggar. God was so impressed by this act of charity that He made the Sun shine and the winds drop until St Martin could get another cloak.

Traditionally, St Martin's summer lasts three and a bit days. Measurements taken at Kew during most of this century have shown that on 11, 12 and 13 November the maximum temperature was generally above average. St Martin's spontaneous goodness had, it seemed, brought the blessing of a fine spell of weather at the same time in London in most years. But the same study showed that there was an equally marked tendency for the average temperatures on 14 and 15 November to be unseasonably cold. This, of course, can be equally well explained by the legend if God had ensured that St Martin's replacement cloak was very warm indeed.

When the days grow shorter and colder around us, while the rain beats down or the fog hangs dismally, many people today dream of being lucky enough to jet away to sunny places. But not every culture was looking for its place in the sun. *The Golden Bough*, Sir James Frazer's great collection of mythology and anthropology, runs fulsome on the subject. According to him, both the mikados of Japan and the pontiffs of the Zapotecs went to great lengths to avoid sunshine. Both were 'looked upon as a god whom the earth was not worthy to hold nor the sun to shine upon'. And places plagued by almost constant sunshine went to great lengths to keep their great ones out of the sun lest their magnificence slip away. The people of Granada in South America kept their infant leaders locked away for years on end rather than expose them to the sunlight.

Even British folklore shows a healthy lack of enthusiasm for sunshine, particularly in winter. An old Rutland saying maintains that 'when there is sunshine and spring in winter the year will not come good'. Northamptonshire folklore offers 'a green winter makes a fat churchyard'. And the Scots show equal lack of enthusiasm with 'The shepherd would rather see the wolf enter his fold on Candlemas Day than the sun.' Germany has a more impenetrable variation of this in 'The shepherd would rather see his wife enter the stable on Christmas Day than the sun.'

If you're still longing wistfully for sunshine and wishing away the dark winter days, consider the advice of *Enquire Within*, which brought solace and information to so many back in 1894. 'Unseasonal heat and sunshine weakens the system.' Cheering words indeed, which do much to help us appreciate the drizzle and sleet. So bearing in mind all the harmful effects of sunlight on the complexion, keep on preserving your divinity and be grateful for winter's cloudy skies.

Keen weather watchers will cast aside all thoughts of settling by the fire to view the big film on Christmas Day. Instead they will be striding outside to observe the prognostications of nature. Of all the Church festivals, there is more weather lore linked to Christmas than to any other time. This is probably not just because of its importance in the Christian calendar but also the fact that it is not a movable feast, so observations made on the same date over many years may well yield some truth.

A windy Christmas Day is said to indicate a good harvest of fruit the following summer. Sun shining through the trees on Christmas Day means a fine crop is on the way, and snow on Christmas night means a good show of hops next year. Green grass at Christmas brings a frosty Easter and a good harvest.

In fact, there are many weather sayings that link Christmas and Easter, one of the most memorable being the couplet:

> Easter in snow, Christmas in mud;
> Christmas in snow, Easter in mud.

But 'if ice will bear a man before Christmas, it will not bear a goose afterwards'.

One of the most widely held Christmas weather proverbs is the grim 'A green Christmas means a fat churchyard.' This saying may have had a sound basis of truth because, just as a severe Christmas was supposed to mean milder weather to come, so a mild Christmas was also said to indicate a long, severe winter just around the corner.

The whole twelve days of Christmas are linked to a good deal of ancient weather lore. In France there was a tradition in some regions of placing twelve large, round onions, each topped with salt, on a board to represent the twelve months of the coming year. Over the twelve days of Christmas the progress of the salt was closely monitored. If the salt melted on the onion, the month it represented would be wet. If the salt remained, that onion's month would be dry.

So if you are looking for something really interesting to do on Christmas Day and over the following few days, start lining up your onions.

'Double-faced February' has a reputation in weather lore for being, to say the least, changeable. While one old saying looks on the bright side, telling us that 'there is always one fine week in February', a more pessimistic (or realistic?) piece of lore from Surrey warns that 'if bees get out in February, the next day will be windy and rainy'.

One thing you can usually be sure of in February is rain – plenty of it, but at the wrong time of year to be much good for the crops. 'February rain is only good to fill ditches', according to French country tradition, while the expression 'February fill dyke' is a close English equivalent.

There is also a wealth of lore basing forecasts for the months ahead on the kind of weather experienced in February. As with much weather lore, it is based on a pattern of opposites. While one saying has it that 'fogs in February mean frosts in May', another tells us that 'there will be as many frosts in June as there are fogs in February'. This is close enough agreement among the sages of yesteryear to make you begin to think they knew what they were talking about. But another variation has it that 'for every thunderstorm bringing rain in February there will be a cold spell in May' – which, given February's 'fill dyke' reputation, might leave you wondering whether May can ever be anything but frosty.

As is often the case, however, many of the most profound and poetical weather sayings are linked to religious festivals: in February, to the feast of Candlemas, on 2 February.

> If Candlemas Day be fair and bright,
> Winter will have another flight.
> But if Candlemas Day brings cloud and rain,
> Winter is gone and won't come again.

And this, of course, is the origin of the various 'ground-hog' legends, which burst upon public awareness with the eponymous movie about a man caught in a time loop. The original version has it that 'if the ground-hog is sunning himself on the second, he will return to his winter quarters for four more weeks'. That brings us back to the reputation 'double-faced February' has in weather lore for being, to say the least, changeable . . .

The myths are not all linked with seasons and saints. Here are a couple of distinctly fishy tales to round off this survey.

Medicine has already rediscovered the benefits of the medicinal leech, but meteorologists are sadly still failing to take up Dr Merryweather of Whitby's recommendations to set up a chain of leech weather-warning stations along our coastline. Visitors to the Great Exhibition at the Crystal Palace in 1851 were much impressed by the appropriately named Dr Merryweather's leech-operated weather-warning system. His leeches were confined in flasks of water and, it is claimed, could be relied upon to ring a little bell when a tempest was in the air.

Dr Merryweather's work, it has to be said, was not entirely original. He drew on knowledge long held by the Spanish weather watchers of Seville, who believed that there are nine basic positions held by leeches when living in a flask half-filled with water. Each position taken up by a leech was said to indicate a different pattern of coming weather.

To make your own leech barometer, first get an old-fashioned medicinal leech (they make undemanding and easily pleased pets). Then half-fill a large glass flask with water, pop in your leech and observe closely. If the leech crawls up out of the water and clings to the inside of the neck of the flask, then rain is on the way. Staying clear of the water and clinging, as leeches do, to the side of the glass, taking up a half-moon position, indicates storms on the way. Imminent thunder and lightning will, the Spaniards assure us, send your leech into a wild frenzy (by leech standards) of continual movement.

When you wake to find your leech coiled up at the bottom of his flask, calm, fine weather should last all day; but if he suddenly starts to move about, expect a strong wind when he stops. Leeches move slowly to a single spot and stay there when expecting a cold snap, and sensibly stay fixed in that position if freezing weather is about to arrive.

The system may not be quite as crazy as it sounds, since it is quite possible that the leech in her flask of water may be sensitive to changes in atmospheric pressure. The most sanguine piece of weather leech-lore is probably the English saying that the leech always becomes agitated just before a change in the weather, one way or the other. But when your medicinal leech crawls out of the flask entirely and heads for the hills – or the nearest warm flesh – you are on your own.

Fish, at first sight, do not strike most people as perceptive meteorologists; but as predictors of bad weather they are more efficient than many. Folk wisdom that stems from observing the movements of fish is widespread and in many cases perceptively accurate. As many a rain-soaked fisherman will testify, fish really do seem to bite more readily and swim nearer the surface during damp weather.

Henry VIII was said to have kept a tame polar bear at the Tower of London who was often allowed out into the flowing river to fish for salmon, which were then common in the Thames. Whether the king used the polar bear's luck at fishing as an indication of forthcoming wet weather is unknown, but salmon are reputed to rise more than usual at the approach of a storm. They are also said to become more plentiful when there has been heavy rain in the surrounding countryside. Other fish become more frisky before rain. Loach and eels are noted for being particularly lively, while pike reverse the trend and lurk silently on the river bed if they sense a storm to be on the way.

More intellectual marine creatures seem even better at predicting the weather. Folk tales involving the abilities of porpoises and dolphins to forecast storms are particularly common. Even Dante's *Inferno* warms to the subject:

> As dolphins heave their backs above the wave,
> Prognosticating angry tempests black.

Sailors have traditionally thought that when dolphins and porpoises gather around a ship and frolic on the surface of the water bad weather is brewing. This belief was so strong that dolphins became regarded as an unlucky omen. On a smaller and possibly duller scale, cuttlefish swimming on the surface also predict storms, and air bubbles over a clam bed are said to be sure indicators of rain.

For an ultimately fishy story: the *Athenaeum* magazine on 17 July 1841 reported a torrential thunderstorm that had recently occurred in London. Intense rain had fallen along with lumps of half-melted ice and an abundance of fish, some weighing almost three ounces. Many were picked up alive but most did not survive falling down on to the pavement. This seems a hard fate for a fish with an aptitude for weather prediction.

The old expression 'raining cats and dogs' has little to do with mammals falling from the sky and everything to do with old Norse mythology. Witches riding on storm clouds were thought to assume the form of cats, while both the dog and the wolf were, in Norse mythology, the attendants of Odin, the god of storms. Strong winds were represented as blowing from the mouth of a wolf. Together, the 'cats and dogs' symbolise downpouring rain and strong blasts of wind.

Sometimes animals rather smaller than cats and dogs really do fall from the sky in showers of rain. On 17 June 1939 *The Times* reported that Trowbridge in Wiltshire had 'been visited by a shower of frogs'. An eyewitness, the attendant of the municipal swimming pool, reported seeing hundreds of tiny frogs falling with the rain on to the concrete path surrounding the open-air bath, each one about the size of the top of a joint of a finger.

The report led to correspondence in which one old India hand recalled a violent storm in Madras in November 1911, which left the ground covered with thousands of tiny frogs, while another veteran recalled that in 1884 Royal Engineers working to prepare the way for the expedition to relieve General Gordon in Khartoum were camped in the desert when a torrential rainstorm deposited 'millions' of frogs of all sizes on the surrounding barren landscape.

Fish, toads, small crabs and winkles have all also been reliably reported falling from the sky, all fresh and some of them ending up in the cooking-pot and duly being eaten. On 28 May 1881, periwinkles, small crabs and hermit crabs were deposited on the streets of Worcester (not a noted seaside resort) during a violent thunderstorm, in quantities described by the *Worcester Evening Post* as 'tons'. Ten sacks of periwinkles were gathered and sold in the local market, and one man alone collected two sacks full from his own garden.

Presumably, these bizarre phenomena are the result of tornadoes or waterspouts lifting aquatic creatures into the air along with the water, but it is still far from clear how such large quantities of living creatures can be transported to locations so far from their source before falling back to Earth.

And finally – does seaweed really predict the weather?

When winter comes on, we become increasingly keen on predicting whether or not it is going to rain. Being caught in a summer shower has its drawbacks, but being buffeted by a freezing downpour when you have forgotten your raincoat is even worse. The meteorologists say they get the forecast right most of the time, but just in case you want a second opinion, how much value can you place in traditional harbingers of rain?

Looking hopefully at that piece of seaweed brought back from summer days at the beach is unlikely to be much help. A bit of kelp can help you observe changes in the weather but it can't predict them. When the weather is dry the moisture in seaweed evaporates, leaving it brittle and hard. In humid weather, kelp absorbs moisture from the air and rehydrates to become soft and pliable again. Seaweed reacts to humidity, but humidity doesn't always mean rain is coming. Mist and fog are extremely humid, for example, but they are often followed by bright, dry weather.

One way of predicting wet weather is to go out and look for a halo around the Moon. 'The Moon with a circle brings water in her beak' is a proverb believed in Greece for over 2,000 years. Haloes around the moon look like luminous rings. They are produced by the refraction of light through ice crystals, and cirrostratus clouds that often mark the leading edge of a warm front are full of ice crystals. These warm fronts often produce rain, but unfortunately, haloes around the Moon are very common and don't always mean that rain and storms are coming; but if you are a keen weather watcher and like to read the signs around you before you decide which coat to wear, looking for a halo around the Moon could well prove more accurate than reaching for the seaweed.

SECRET PLAN TO MELT THE ICE·CAPS.

GRASS → [cow] → CH₄

7

LIVING IN A GREENHOUSE

Just at the time when meteorologists think they have developed a good understanding of the natural processes behind wind and weather, a spanner has been thrown in the forecasting works by human activities. Future weather patterns are likely to be significantly different from those of the recent past, and correspondingly harder to predict, largely because of the anthropogenic greenhouse effect. The main culprit is carbon dioxide, produced by burning fossil fuel.

We owe our knowledge that the amount of carbon dioxide in the air has been increasing since the mid-1950s to one man, Charles Keeling. Without his pioneering work, the link between rising concentrations of atmospheric carbon dioxide and rising global temperatures might still be 'just a theory'.

Keeling stumbled on his life's work almost by accident. He left Northwestern University, Illinois, in 1954, with a PhD in chemistry. While most of his fellow 'postdocs' were heading into industry to, as he put it, 'make breakfast cereals crisper, gasoline more powerful, plastics cheaper, and antibiotics more expensive', Keeling, a keen back-packer, decided to find work that involved the great out-doors. He talked his way into the then-new geochemistry research programme at the California Institute of Technology, and, largely on the grounds that the work couldn't be done indoors, set up a programme to monitor the amount of carbon dioxide in the air.

The original plan was to see if the amount of carbon dioxide in streams and lakes was the same as in the air above. But to do this, Keeling had to build an accurate detector to measure traces of carbon dioxide in the air. He then became compulsively obsessed with taking measurements, day and night, everywhere he went, including on the laboratory roof while waiting for his wife to give birth to their son.

He found that the amount of carbon dioxide in the air in a forest varies from day to night as the trees 'breathe', but that there is an underlying base concentration, which itself changes with the seasons. As early as 1955, he had set the benchmark for this global average concentration, before anyone was worrying about the greenhouse effect, at 315 parts per million.

The next step was triggered, serendipitously, by the International Geophysical Year, 1956–7. As his contri-bution to this effort, Keeling designed new instruments to monitor carbon dioxide continuously, from a mountaintop in Hawaii. And that is why we know that the amount of carbon dioxide has been rising steadily since 1955 and has now passed 360 parts per million.

Most public concern about the threat of global warming caused by the 'greenhouse effect' of gases such as carbon dioxide focuses, understandably enough, on timescales of fifty to a hundred years. Within the next century, human activities are likely to double the amount of carbon dioxide in the air. Optimists say that this will raise global average temperatures by only a degree or so (Celsius), while pessimists say that temperatures may rise by 3°C within a human lifetime.

What of the longer perspective? Unless industrial activity grinds to a complete halt, the concentration of greenhouse gases in the atmosphere will continue to rise long after the end of the twenty-first century. Two researchers based in the United States, Syukuro Manabe and Ronald Stouffer, have calculated just what that might eventually mean for life on Earth.

They have calculated the effects of quadrupling the amount of carbon dioxide in the air over the next 140 years, and then holding the concentration steady until the year 2500. Average temperatures would rise by 7°C as a result, but this is only the beginning of the story.

In the oceans today, water at high latitudes cools so much that it becomes heavy and sinks into the depths, initiating a 'conveyor belt' of circulation that carries water around the globe and takes dissolved oxygen down below the surface. Global warming on the scale likely beyond the next century would reduce this activity by 90 per cent.

Today, microscopic inhabitants of the sea absorb carbon dioxide from the air during photosynthesis, and the cold, sinking water itself dissolves carbon dioxide and carries it into the depths. If all this activity stops, one of the main natural 'sinks' removing carbon dioxide from the air will become inactive.

The result will be that even without further human intervention global warming will take off again (from a state 7°C warmer than today) as carbon dioxide builds up in the air. And this prospect is as close to us in time as the birth of Shakespeare.

Carbon dioxide is not the only gas that causes
global warming through the greenhouse effect,
but the complexity of climate forecasts was
highlighted by one side-effect of the collapse
of the Soviet Union.

One of the strongest greenhouse gases, methane, is not
building up as rapidly as before in the Earth's atmosphere.
The reason may be the collapse of the old Soviet empire:
methane is a major component of natural gas, which used
to escape in large quantities from the rickety pipeline network of Eastern Europe. But now the countries of the
former Soviet Union and its satellites simply cannot afford
to waste this resource.

The slackening of the build-up of methane in the air
has been discovered by an Australian researcher, Graeme
Pearman, working with British and American colleagues.
In the 1970s, the amount of methane in the air was building
up at a rate of just over 1 per cent a year, but by the end
of the 1980s the build-up was proceeding only half as fast.
In the mid-1990s, it has practically stopped.

This is good news because methane is far more efficient
at trapping heat than the most notorious greenhouse gas,
carbon dioxide. One molecule of methane holds in twenty
times more warmth near the ground than a single molecule
of carbon dioxide. Carbon dioxide is still the principal
worry as far as global warming is concerned, because there
is much more of it around.

Even so, overall the amount of methane in the air has
tripled since 1945, to just under 2 parts per million, and
its influence cannot be ignored. The world is probably
about a quarter of a degree (Celsius) warmer than it would
be if there were no methane in the atmosphere.

Economic changes in the former Soviet empire cannot
be the whole story, because methane is also produced

naturally, and by agricultural activities, especially from rice paddies (it is sometimes known as 'swamp gas'). It has been building up steadily in the atmosphere since the agricultural revolution about 300 years ago that started the rapid growth in the human population of the world. Something, it seems, must actually be taking methane out of the air to bring its build-up to a halt, since rice paddies certainly are not being taken out of production.

One of the other problems with long-range forecasting is unravelling natural changes from the influence of human activities.

Critics of predictions of global warming based on the greenhouse effect often point to the region around the North Atlantic Ocean. There, up to the beginning of the 1990s, temperatures failed to rise in line with calculations of the impact of greenhouse gases over the past half century. And yet, the world as a whole *has* warmed by 0.5°C in the past hundred years. How can these facts be reconciled?

According to researchers at the University of Illinois, the cause is a natural climate fluctuation that depressed temperatures over the North Atlantic, North America and Europe just at the time when the greenhouse effect was beginning to push them higher. This climate cycle was found by subtracting out the long-term trend in global temperature from records going back to 1858 and using a statistical technique to analyse the variations that were left.

To find out which parts of the world are moving out of step with the overall warming, Michael Schlesinger and Navin Ramankutty divided the globe into eleven regions. There is a natural temperature oscillation over the North Atlantic taking seventy-six years to complete one cycle, and producing a fluctuation of about three-quarters of a degree. There are similar fluctuations, with similar periods and magnitude, affecting North America, Eurasia, and Africa.

More research will be needed to find out what causes these fluctuations. They may just be natural oscillations of the weather system, like the natural vibrations of a guitar string, or they may be linked with changes in the Sun's activity.

Whatever its cause, the key feature of the North Atlantic fluctuation is that it reached a peak around 1950 and then declined until the late 1980s. Other things being equal, that would have produced a cooling of more than half a degree. But since the end of the 1980s, the natural fluctuation has begun adding to any global warming caused by the build-up of greenhouse gases.

If the Illinois researchers are correct, that means that after four decades without a dramatic warming, our part of the world will be rapidly catching up with the rest of the globe over the next twenty years.

The weather watchers on the top of a Hawaiian mountain have found another odd climate correlation. Just after the eruption of the Pinatubo volcano in 1991, the build-up of carbon dioxide in the atmosphere temporarily went into reverse.

Worldwide, more carbon dioxide was released into the air each year in the early 1990s than ever; but even more was taken out of the atmosphere in 1992 and 1993 by some unknown 'sink'.

The build-up of carbon dioxide has been monitored in the clean Pacific air on the Hawaiian mountain Mauna Loa since 1957, and this is the first such reverse to have occurred since then. Usually, about half of the carbon dioxide produced each year by human activities is absorbed by natural processes (including being dissolved in the sea) and the rest stays in the air.

The carbon dioxide 'lost' in those two years must have gone somewhere. The researchers involved in the measurements, who work at the University of California in San Diego, have suggested that it has been absorbed by an increase in biological activity. But if the timing of the change is not just a coincidence, they have to explain how the eruption of a volcano in the Pacific could trigger such activity.

Like land plants, microscopic sea plants take up carbon dioxide during photosynthesis, as they absorb energy from the Sun. Studies carried out recently have shown that the growth of these oceanic organisms is often limited by the amount of iron available. They have all the food they need, and plenty of sunlight, but cannot grow more without iron compounds.

One possibility is that the spreading dust cloud from the Pinatubo eruption dropped enough iron in the ocean to stimulate a burst of growth of these organisms. Pinatubo released 500 million tonnes of iron in the cloud of debris from the eruption, and only 0.02 per cent of this would be enough to do the trick, if it were all taken up by life in the sea.

More about this 'iron fertilisation' effect shortly. Meanwhile, quite apart from this odd correlation, by cooling the globe, the Pinatubo eruption actually confirmed the reliability of the computer models that predict global warming.

The cooling effect of the Mount Pinatubo eruption in 1991 was less than predicted, because the Earth is responding to the greenhouse effect more strongly than had been thought.

The world warmed by about 0.5°C in the hundred years up to 1990, and most climatologists have linked this to the build-up of greenhouse gases. But natural climatic variations are still at work, and this was vividly demonstrated by the Pinatubo eruption, which created a temporary sun shield. The experts expected that this would cool the Earth by about half a degree by the end of 1992, almost exactly cancelling out the recent warming, before the volcanic debris cleared and the warming renewed. But the climate figures for 1992 and 1993 actually showed that there was a cooling of only about 0.3°C to the end of 1992, and that temperatures began to rise again in 1993, even though there was still some volcanic material in the upper atmosphere.

The implication is that the increasing greenhouse effect overwhelmed part of the anticipated volcanic cooling. With the effects of Pinatubo completely faded from the climate system, in the mid-1990s temperatures returned to the record-breaking levels of the late 1980s. If nothing else happens to produce a downward blip in temperatures on the same sort of scale as the Pinatubo eruption, we can expect new record temperatures to be set in the late 1990s.

Forget, for a moment, the arguments about whether the world as a whole has warmed slightly, and why. The best indication of whether the greenhouse effect is at work, says David Thomson of the American AT&T Bell Laboratories is the pronounced shift in the seasons that has taken place in the northern hemisphere since 1940.

Bell Labs is a research centre run by the AT&T telephone and communications company, and Thomson is an expert at processing data to extract the information – the 'signals'

– they contain. He has now applied these signal-processing techniques to long runs of temperature data from single sites, including one in central England that goes back to 1651. Unlike other researchers, he is not interested in the annual average temperatures but in the differences between the seasons from one year to the next.

From the 1650s to the 1940s, the pattern of the seasonal temperature cycle changed by no more than a day in each century. But since 1940 there has been a noticeable change in the pattern.

The simplest way to see this is in terms of the timing of the hottest days of the year. In the northern hemisphere, we get maximum heat from the Sun on the 'longest day', 22 June; but the Earth is closest to the Sun in its orbit on 3 January. So southern summers are (other things being equal) slightly hotter than northern summers.

As heat is carried around the world by winds and ocean currents, there is a slight tendency for seasonal differences to be smoothed out in the northern hemisphere. The situation isn't quite that simple, because you also have to allow for the different rates at which oceans and continents respond to solar heating. But, according to Thomson, once that is allowed for, seasonal extremes have recently got more pronounced, with the peak northern warmth more sharply concentrated near the end of June.

Because greenhouse gases such as carbon dioxide work by trapping heat from the Sun, this is exactly what should be expected if the greenhouse effect is getting stronger. And the only time this effect has shown up in the record spanning three centuries is in the past fifty years.

Some people may be sceptical about all this;
but simpler creatures, following their instincts,
know what is happening to the weather.

One of the best indicators of global warming has been discovered by Trevor Beebee of the University of Sussex. It is the spawning time of amphibians – toads, frogs and, especially, newts – in southern England.

All the British amphibians migrate to their breeding ponds in spring, and those in the warm south-west do so earlier than those in the cold north-east. Beebee and his colleagues have been studying two breeding sites closely since 1978. One, in Hampshire, is a favoured haunt of natterjack toads, at the northern limit of their range in Britain where they may well be most sensitive to climate change. The other, in Sussex, is used by a profusion of species, including two kinds of frog and three kinds of newt.

All but one of the species studied showed a significant change in breeding habits over the seventeen years since 1978, spawning earlier in later years. But the newts showed by far the most dramatic change, arriving at their breeding ponds on average five to seven weeks earlier in 1990–94 than they had been in 1978–82.

Hardly surprisingly, these behavioural changes correlated well with changes in the local climate over the same period. The average maximum March – April temperatures at the first site increased at a rate of 0.11°C per year from 1978 to 1994, while at the second site the average maximum temperature increased by 0.24°C per year in the crucial months for the newts. The breeding activity of the species involved got earlier at a rate corresponding to about ten days for every 1°C rise in the relevant maximum temperatures.

This, says Beebee, suggests 'that amphibian reproductive

cycles in temperate countries can respond sensitively to climate change', and that studies of this kind, 'should be a useful biological indicator of long-term climate change', because monitoring of this kind is relatively simple to carry out.

Next time you see one of those roadside signs warning of toads crossing, make a note of the date. By the year 2000, those signs may have to be erected a week earlier than they have been recently.

Natural climatic changes over the past 14,000 years have given American biologists a chance to observe evolution at work. They have found that the body size of the North American woodrat reduces dramatically from generation to generation when the world warms.

How do you know how big a woodrat was 19,000 years ago? Not by measuring fossilised skeletons, which simply don't exist (the woodrats were too tasty a morsel for other creatures for that). Instead, a team from the University of New Mexico and the US Geological Survey has been measuring the sizes of what they delicately refer to as 'faecal pellets' preserved in the deposits from different centuries and dated using the carbon-14 technique.

Woodrats are gregarious creatures and live in middens where they deposit a lot of rubbish, including, in the words of the US team, 'copious faecal pellets and other materials embedded in crystallised urine', which lay undisturbed in caves for tens of thousands of years. Studies of present-day woodrats show that the width of the faecal pellets is closely related to the body size of the rat, so all you have to do is measure the crystallised pellets to find out how big the rats used to be, on average.

The evidence is conclusive. At the end of the latest Ice Age, 14,000 years ago, the biggest woodrat living in a particular cave in Utah weighed in at about 430 grams. By 6,000 years ago, the rats' descendants were all less than 300 grams in weight, reflecting the global warming out of the Ice Age. But since then the rats have got slightly bigger, as the world cooled a little.

Overall, the variation is at least 20 per cent in mass, more than a quarter of the entire variation of woodrat body size seen today from Canada to Arizona. It is possible that some of the change reflects migration, as smaller woodrats move north when the world warms. But the researchers find this hard to believe, given the rats' sedentary life style and the speed with which the changes occurred.

Some creatures find it harder to cope.

The latest victims of global warming are moths. No, they are not going down with heatstroke; the problem is that carbon dioxide is throwing their nervous systems out of kilter.

Researchers at the Australian National University have been looking at the way different concentrations of carbon dioxide affect the moth *Helicoverpa armigera*, which is a major agricultural pest. The moths have receptors in their mouths which are sensitive to the amount of carbon dioxide in the air. Detecting carbon dioxide is important to the moths because it helps them to find their food: they can measure fluctuations in its concentration caused by the metabolic activity of the plants they feed on and can home in on the source of the 'signal'.

In most insects, receptor neurons of this kind are strongly affected by temperature and work efficiently only for a certain range of temperatures. But the researchers found that the carbon dioxide receptors in this particular moth have a built-in system that compensates for changes in temperature. Provided that the background concentration of carbon dioxide is between 250 and 300 parts per million, they can compensate for temperature variations.

The problem for the moths is that the background concentration of carbon dioxide, thanks to human activities, is now above 360 parts per million and rising fast. It used to be about 280 parts per million, before people started destroying forests and burning fossil fuel in large quantities, and the concentration fluctuated naturally between 190 and 290 parts per million during the latest series of Ice Age cycles, going back millions of years.

So the moths, which are well adapted to the natural environment, are living in a world which is moving the goalposts out of their range. As carbon dioxide continues to increase in the atmosphere, the effect will be to cause the moth's receptors to mistake temperature fluctuations for changes in carbon dioxide concentrations, sending it off in the wrong direction in its search for food. Bad news for the moths, but possibly not for farmers, who will be glad to see the back of them.

The non-living world is also shaped by the changing climate.

In 1972, before widespread concern about global warming was expressed, geographers at a conference organised by the International Geographical Union were surprised to discover that although all of them knew of many sandy beaches that were eroding, scarcely any of them knew of any regions of the world where sandy beaches were getting wider. Curious to know whether the effect was real, or simply a subjective piece of hearsay, they set up a survey involving 129 researchers and every country with a sea coast.

The researchers used old maps and charts, written descriptions of how the coast looked in the past, and modern air and ground photographs. They worked out how every major sandy beach in the world had changed in recent decades, and by the end of the 1970s they had concluded that the effect was real. The world's beaches are vanishing.

More than 70 per cent of the total length of sandy coast-line around the world has shrunk at a rate of at least 10 cm per year during most of the twentieth century. Less than 10 per cent of the world's sandy coast is growing, and the remaining 20 per cent has stayed much the same.

By the time the results of the survey were announced, in the early 1980s, climatologists had begun to worry about the possibility of global warming. They pointed out that average temperatures had risen by nearly 0.5°C since the end of the nineteenth century, and that over the same period sea level has risen by about 10 cm.

The sea level rise is strong additional evidence that the global warming is real, because this rise of 10 cm is exactly what should be produced if the top layer of the oceans had warmed by about half a degree, and expanded as a result. The rise is *not* caused by melting ice-caps, but simply by thermal expansion. In exactly the same way, if you carefully measure a mugful of cold milk, then pour the milk into a pan and heat it nearly to boiling point, you will find that you now have too much milk to fit back into the mug.

Rising sea level neatly explains the retreat of the sandy beaches – so the vanishing beaches are also a sign of global warming. But the real problem is not that the beaches are being eroded from the sea side. Rather, it is that they have nowhere to grow on the land side.

When sea level has risen in the past, beaches would move bodily inland. But now there are sea walls, roads, houses and industrial sites along the coast. When the sea rises it washes away the old beach, but sand cannot push inland to make a new one.

The problem is worse along the Atlantic coast of the United States. Many towns grew up there alongside ocean beaches. Very often, the word 'beach' is still a part of the town's name, even though the beach itself has vanished. Miami Beach in Florida is a good example. There, however, when the beach washed away, the city authorities built a new one with sand sucked up from the sea floor, in order to keep the tourists coming in.

Now that the threat of global warming caused by a build-up of carbon dioxide in the air is firmly established, many researchers are turning their attention to finding ways of removing this greenhouse gas from the air. If enough carbon dioxide can be taken out of the atmosphere and stored away safely, we can all carry on burning fossil fuel without the world overheating.

'Technofix' solutions to the greenhouse effect have to overcome one big hurdle: extracting carbon dioxide from the air requires energy. So you have to burn more fuel to extract the carbon dioxide. Assuming the process can be made cost-effective, however, the neatest solution to the greenhouse problem is to pump liquefied carbon dioxide into the natural reservoirs below ground from which oil is being pumped out today.

The favoured technofix is to dump carbon dioxide, either in liquid or solid form, at the bottom of the sea. It is denser than water, and would sink out of sight, if not entirely out of mind. Dumped from pipelines extending 3 km below sea level, the carbon dioxide would stay submerged for hundreds of years, giving our descendants (it is hoped) time to decide what to do when ocean currents eventually bring it back to the surface.

But the neatest proposed solution to the global warming problem involves less technology and more of nature lending a hand. Microscopic plants living in the sea already absorb large quantities of carbon dioxide during photosynthesis. Some of this is turned into the chalky shells of these organisms, and when they die the shells fall to the seabed, locking up the carbon dioxide in chalk sediments.

Recently, researchers discovered that these plankton grow more vigorously if dosed with solutions containing iron, which is an essential ingredient for photosynthesis. Could we solve the greenhouse problem by spreading iron compounds across the oceans?

A team from the Netherlands and Germany has proved that iron fertilisation works by letting nature do the experiment for them.

There have been speculations that at least part of the reason why Ice Ages are cold is that plankton are more active then, drawing more carbon dioxide out of the air.

Iron comes into the story because, the argument runs, continents dry out during Ice Ages, and dry winds blow dust carrying more than a trace of iron out over the oceans. And plankton need iron to make the very chlorophyll that they use in photosynthesis. Everything fits, in theory. But where is it happening in practice?

The Dutch–German team has found the answer. In the southern ocean, near Antarctica, there are regions (between 50° and 60° South) where currents with quite different origins run alongside each other. They experience the same amount of sunlight, and are subject to the same amount of cloud cover. But one current is fed by water containing only a moderate amount of iron, welling up from the deep ocean near the Weddell Sea, while the other current, just to the north, is much richer in iron compounds.

Sure enough, the team found that in the southern spring the plankton grow more vigorously, or 'bloom', in the iron-rich current, where, as a result, there is a much lower concentration of dissolved carbon dioxide. 'Iron availability,' they say, 'was the critical factor in allowing the blooms to occur.'

So iron fertilisation works, at least in nature.
It also works when humans lend a hand. But
not, unfortunately, well enough to be a 'fix'
for the problem of the greenhouse effect.

The original suggestion (actually made by one of us, JG, in the journal *Nature*, vol. 331, 1988, p. 570) came when marine biologists noticed that adding compounds rich in iron to samples of sea water in the lab produced an explosive growth of plankton. The plankton had plenty of everything else they needed in order to grow, but lacked iron, an important ingredient of chlorophyll.

Wouldn't it be nice, that contribution to *Nature* suggested, if iron could be spread across the oceans in sufficient quantities to cause a boom in plant growth, sucking carbon dioxide out of the air and reducing the greenhouse effect? The first tests of the idea have now been carried out, by researchers from Duke University, in North Carolina.

In the experiment, 480 kilos of iron, in the form of iron sulphate solution, were dumped into the sea 500 km south of the Galapagos Islands. The iron was added over a period of twenty-four hours and was churned well into the ocean by the propellors of the researchers' ship as it steamed to and fro.

Initial results were 'spectacular', in the words of the team; but they were short-lived. Chlorophyll concentration increased, and the amount of plankton and its rate of production both doubled in the patch of ocean in three days.

But after four days the iron started to disappear, dropping out of solution and forming tiny particles that sank into the ocean depths. As it did so, the plankton activity returned to normal.

All of which leaves marine biologists happy that they have found a new feature of the oceanic life chain, but climatologists back at square one in their search for a greenhouse fix – unless someone knows how to make iron float.

If iron won't do the trick, other 'fertilisers' might.

Would-be fixers of the carbon dioxide greenhouse effect have found another possible way in which to encourage the uptake of carbon dioxide by the oceans. It seems that zinc, as well as iron, is needed for the healthy growth of those tiny marine organisms known as phytoplankton, which absorb carbon dioxide during photosynthesis.

A team at the Massachusetts Institute of Technology has been finding alternative ways to fertilise the oceans. Their latest discovery is that extra zinc in the water encourages the growth of phytoplankton under laboratory conditions, or rather 'that low zinc availability may limit the growth of oceanic phytoplankton'.

According to the MIT team, zinc has a greater potential to produce a larger impact on the global carbon cycle than iron has, because other elements are needed in conjunction with iron to make chlorophyll. Zinc is used by phytoplankton in chemical processes that also require carbon, but the whole point of this research is that there is too much carbon around, in the form of carbon dioxide.

This, it now seems, may explain why there was much less carbon dioxide in the air during the latest Ice Age than there is today.

Because the Ice Age climate was dry, winds would have carried dusty material containing iron and zinc compounds off the continents and out to sea, providing fertiliser that kept the phytoplankton in bloom and sucked carbon dioxide out of the air, helping to maintain the Ice Age cold by reducing the greenhouse effect.

8

HUMAN
IMPACTS

*Although the greenhouse effect is likely to
have the biggest impact on climate change in
the twenty-first century, there are other
human activities that affect the weather,
including one long dismissed as a myth.*

Could those old wives' tales about nuclear weapons testing
affecting the weather be true after all? K. Y. Kondratyev
and G. A. Nikolsky from Leningrad/St Petersburg have
puzzled over the reason why the world cooled sharply in
the early 1960s. They conclude that the cause may have
been a flurry of atmospheric nuclear testing by the super-
powers in the run-up to the partial test ban treaty of 1963.

Kondratyev and Nikolsky found that instruments
carried high into the stratosphere by balloons had recorded
a depletion of ozone in the stratosphere between about
1960 and 1964, just when the world below was cooling.
The ozone layer then recovered rapidly during the second
half of the 1960s, as the world below warmed out of the
cold spell that had lasted from 1958 to 1964. The cooling
had reduced the average temperature of the northern
hemisphere by half a degree Celsius.

The winter of 1962–3 was memorably cold in Europe, and over the hemisphere as a whole the winter of 1963–4 was even colder. The possible explanation is that pollution caused by nuclear weapons testing caused both the loss of ozone and the cooling.

The argument runs like this. Ozone is destroyed by chemical reactions involving sunlight. These reactions occur more readily if there are oxides of nitrogen in the atmosphere. Atmospheric nuclear explosions make a lot of nitrogen oxides, by burning nitrogen from the air with oxygen from the air. And the nuclear fireball reaches heights of 30 to 45 km above the ground, in the heart of the stratosphere. This triggers ozone-destroying reactions. But because the reactions that destroy ozone involve sunlight, they 'use up' some of the sunlight that would otherwise pass through the stratosphere and warm the surface of the Earth.

According to Kondratyev and Nikolsky, by the beginning of 1963 there was pollution resulting from the explosion of 980 megatons of nuclear bombs still in the stratosphere, reducing by 2.5 per cent the amount of solar heat getting through the ozone layer. The claim is controversial and, short of letting off a few dozen more nuclear bombs in the atmosphere to see what happens, it cannot be tested. But if there is any truth in the Russian calculations, they may also apply to the effect of nitrogen oxides produced by the exhausts of high-flying supersonic aircraft such as Concorde and its proposed successors.

In the days of atmospheric testing of nuclear bombs, many people used to worry – it now seems rightly! – about the effects of such large explosions on the weather. Today, when severe storms seem to be increasingly common in Britain, the question can be turned on its head: just how much energy does a severe North Atlantic depression hurl our way, compared with an atomic bomb? The answer is, 'a lot'; but nowhere near as much as a tropical hurricane.

A severe storm roaring up the English Channel (or down

the North Sea) might have as much energy as a moderate-size atomic bomb, the same kind of weapon that was used to destroy Hiroshima and Nagasaki. In those terms, the storm's destructive power would be equivalent to maybe 20 kilotons of TNT, but, of course, spread out over a wider area than a nuclear explosion.

A tropical hurricane, on the other hand, releases an incredible 10 trillion trillion (a 1 followed by 25 noughts) ergs of energy every second, according to the *Encyclopaedia Britannica*. But how can we relate these incomprehensibly large numbers to everyday life?

Let's start with a kiloton. That would be equivalent to a trillion calories, enough to heat 10,000 tons of water from freezing-point to boiling-point. A healthy storm expends twenty times that energy.

But the energies of hydrogen (or fusion) bombs are measured in tens of megatons, not kilotons. And even that only begins to give us the sort of number we need to understand the power of the largest hurricanes.

Converting calories into ergs, dividing by megatons and taking away the number you first thought of, that incomprehensible number for the energy released in a full-blown hurricane works out as equivalent to exploding one of the largest hydrogen bombs ever tested *every second*. You could literally explode a hydrogen bomb in the middle of such a storm without its having any noticeable effect on it.

That, of course, is why meteorologists poured scorn on the notion that nuclear weapons tests could affect the weather of the world. Even a tropical hurricane represents only a small cog in the entire weather machine, which is actually driven by the heat of the Sun. What they hadn't realised was that the nuclear tests might have affected the input of heat from that solar engine to the weather machine.

*Some human impacts on weather are more
subtle, and more down-to-Earth.*

It's now more than forty years since the most killing 'pea-souper' smog – fog polluted with smoke – hit London in December 1952. That smog alone killed an estimated 2,850 people from bronchitis and pneumonia, and is remembered as the worst smog ever to affect the city.

Since 1952, London's air quality has improved, thanks to legislation restricting the use of smoky fuels and to the decline of dirty industrial activity in and around the capital. But other urban regions have not been so lucky. In the 1990s, cities such as Tokyo and Mexico City are at risk from a worse kind of pollution, the photochemical smog created by chemical reactions involving exhaust fumes from vehicles and sunlight. These smogs arise in summer, not winter, producing a build-up of ozone, nitrogen oxides and other compounds that make your eyes water and cause coughing. In extreme cases, photochemical smogs, like the pea-soupers of old, also kill.

One reason why little effective action has been taken to curb photochemical smog in many parts of the world is that it is harder to see than the old pea-soupers. The smog that blanketed London for five days in December 1952 was so thick that people on the Isle of Dogs literally could not see their feet and several walked straight into the river. Tales are also told of theatre-goers in the West End who, after struggling to find first the theatre and then their seats, complained that they could not see what was happening on stage!

The root cause of that pea-souper was, in fact, the same as the root cause of modern photochemical smogs. In both cases, a layer of cooler air gets trapped underneath a layer of warmer air. This is known as a temperature inversion, because normally air at ground level is warmer than the air above. As every schoolchild knows, hot air rises. So if cold air lies under hot air, it cannot rise, and pollutants build up at ground level where they do their worst.

In London, inversions commonly occur in winter, when the cold ground chills the air near it; in Mexico City or Los Angeles, the local geography helps to trap air near the ground in summer, while the air at higher altitudes warms and acts like a lid on the polluted air.

So far, no photochemical smog is known to have killed as many people as London's pea-souper of 1952. But that may only be because nobody is keeping the right statistics. After all, the first sign that something was seriously wrong in 1952 came only when the undertakers reported that they were running out of coffins.

*And then there are those bright ideas which,
on reflection, turn out not to be so clever.*

Researchers from Chile and Canada who thought they had perfected an infallible new technique to obtain drinking water in arid regions are having to think again. They have discovered, to paraphrase Robert Heinlein, that 'there ain't no such thing as a free drink'.

The great idea, hailed as the first new method of providing drinking water since desalination was invented in the 1860s, involves catching the moisture in fog. The technique has been perfected in the hills of the Atacama Desert, in northern Chile, where there may be no rain for several years at a time, but where fog banks regularly roll in from the Pacific Ocean.

Trapping the moisture in the fog turned out to be disarmingly simple, once somebody had the bright idea. Large sheets of plastic mesh (each 12 metres by 4 metres) are strung out in a line along a ridge, square on to the prevailing wind and about 2 metres above the ground. Moisture from the fog condenses on to the plastic, trickles down to a collecting trough, and eventually to the village of Cgungungo, where the people previously relied on water brought in by trucks.

Each square metre of mesh provides between three and four litres of fresh water a day, and the technique could be applied in many arid regions around the world, such as Namibia, where there is a suitable combination of a nearby ocean, the right prevailing wind and plenty of fog. But there is a catch.

The fog captured by the plastic nets 'ought' to be going on inland, and dropping its modest burden of moisture on to the ground. In some parts of Namibia, for example, such fog provides half of the annual precipitation, and it can be relied on to come every year, unlike the rains. These arid regions may not be lush, but they are home to specially adapted plants, helping to maintain an ecology balanced on the proverbial knife-edge. Take away half of the water supply, and a region that was arid but alive could become a lifeless desert.

As long as the new technique is restricted to keeping the villagers of Cgungungo in water, no great harm will be done. But the technique is never likely to rival desalination on a large scale.

There's bad news about the successful efforts in recent years to reduce atmospheric pollution. The particles of dust and droplets of liquid – collectively known as aerosols – put into the atmosphere from factory and power-station chimneys may have been protecting us from solar ultraviolet radiation.

A new study suggests that in industrialised countries the amount of biologically harmful UVB radiation reaching the ground has decreased by between 5 and 18 per cent since the beginning of the industrial revolution, chiefly as a result of dioxide emissions.

The estimate has been made by S. C. Liu of the US National Oceanic and Atmospheric Administration, S. A. McKean of the University of Colorado and S. Madronich of the US National Center for Atmospheric Research, all based in Boulder, Colorado.

They have used measurements of the scattering of sunlight caused by aerosols over the eastern United States, together with calculations using a computer model, to simulate conditions at latitude 40°N with average summer (July) weather. They conclude that 'in urban and rural locations of industrialised regions such as the eastern US and Europe, and probably most of the populated areas in other developed countries' aerosols 'have reduced UVB levels significantly since the industrial revolution and offset the increases in UVB expected from current stratospheric ozone depletion'.

The significance of this is that UVB is a cause of skin cancer and eye cataracts. It also damages plants, which are especially vulnerable to UVB when they are young seedlings growing in spring.

Although the Sun produces ultraviolet radiation which reaches the top of the Earth's atmosphere, most of this is absorbed by ozone in the stratosphere, between 15 kilometres and 50 kilometres above our heads, and never reaches the ground. But if there is less ozone in the stratosphere, more UVB will penetrate to the Earth's surface. This is why there has been so much concern about damage to the ozone layer of the stratosphere caused by the release of ozone-depleting chemicals such as CFCs.

R. L. McKenzie, W. A. Matthews and P. V. Johnston of the DSIR Physical Sciences Laboratory in Otago, New Zealand, have put the risk in perspective. They report measurements which show that a reduction of 1 per cent in the amount of ozone in the stratosphere causes an increase of 1.25 per cent in the amount of biologically active UVB radiation at the surface of the Earth.

During the 1980s, the amount of ozone in the stratosphere above Europe decreased by about 8 per cent. This is attributed to the effect of CFCs released by human activity. Without the shielding effect of pollution in the lower atmosphere, this would have increased the amount of UVB at the surface by 10 per cent, but that shield is now being removed as industry cleans up its act.

As Liu and colleagues put it, 'future coincident reductions in sulphate aerosols and in stratospheric ozone in industrialised countries may result in a stronger positive trend in UVB than expected from either constituent alone'.

Sometimes it is hard to be sure whether human influences or natural causes are to blame.

The drying out of the Aral Sea in central Asia is often held up as an example of the dangers of human interference with nature. It is widely accepted that the sea is drying out because of misguided irrigation schemes planned by the old Soviet bureaucracy, which diverted water on to farmlands and left too little for the sea to maintain itself.

But there is another side to the coin. Not too far from the Aral Sea lies the Caspian Sea, a much larger body of water. And while the Aral Sea has been drying in recent decades, the Caspian has been swelling, inundating habitations around its banks. Between 1977 and 1992, the sea level in the Caspian rose by some two metres.

This seems to fly in the face of human intervention. From the 1930s to the 1970s, with an interruption during the war, great dam-building projects on the rivers that flow into the Caspian (including the mighty Volga) had diverted water while, sure enough, the sea level fell. But in the

1970s and 1980s, there was no let-up in human abstraction of water from the rivers, and yet the sea level rose.

Some wild ideas have been proposed to explain the phenomenon of the seesawing seas. One is that water may be flowing underground from the Aral Sea, which sits 70 metres higher than the Caspian, into its neighbour. But this doesn't, to coin a phrase, hold water. Too little water is being lost from the small Aral Sea to explain the rise in the larger Caspian, while it is quite clear where the extra water in the Caspian is coming from: the Volga and other rivers feeding the sea are flowing more vigorously.

This leaves only one explanation. A climate shift has changed precipitation patterns in the region to drop more water on to the rivers that feed the Caspian, and less in the catchment area of the Aral Sea. And since submerged treetrunks have been found below even the present reduced level of the Aral Sea, it looks as if something similar has happened in the past. For once, the human breastbeating may be misplaced, and sackcloth and ashes need not be called for.

But, of course, it is always possible that the shift in the rainfall patterns is linked with global warming caused by the greenhouse effect . . .

9 A METEOROLOGICAL MISCELLANY

Some of the most fascinating aspects of weather watching defy any attempt at classification.

We've all heard about 'keeping a weather-eye open' – but a weather *ear*? There is, in fact, a difference. A practised weather eye can warn of changes that are about to happen; researchers at the University of Michigan, however, have found a way to use ears to reveal details of past weather and climate.

Not human ears, though. What the American team has done is to develop a new twist on a long-established technique for probing past climates. It depends on the fact that the atoms of oxygen in the air come in two varieties, one slightly heavier than the other, called isotopes. Water molecules contain oxygen, so some water molecules are slightly heavier than others.

Living creatures take up the two kinds of water molecule at different rates, and the exact proportions of heavy and light oxygen that get laid down in their bodies depends in a sensitive way on temperature. So, for example, studies of the chalky shells of long-dead sea creatures have been used to map patterns of temperature variations over hundreds of thousands of years, using cores of chalk drilled from the ocean bed. But this reveals only the broad pattern of climate change, from century to century. The new trick paints with a much finer brush.

The ears of vertebrate animals contain tiny granules of calcium carbonate, known as otoliths. As an animal moves, the otoliths roll about within the ear, triggering sensitive hair cells which signal the movement to the brain.

Fish that live in the freshwater lakes of North America add a new layer of carbonate to their otoliths every day, and by slicing open otoliths from fossil fish, then analysing the tiny fluctuations in oxygen isotopes in different onion-skin layers, the Michigan researchers have begun to paint a picture of temperature variations in Florida 3.5 million years ago.

Fossilised otoliths up to 150 million years old have been discovered, and the next step of the investigation may be to map out the changing weather patterns of a typical year at the time of the dinosaurs.

The weather may also be responsible for human problems that seem, on the face of things, to have a quite different cause.

Between the late thirteenth century and the end of the fourteenth, life expectancy in England fell by about ten years. A principal cause of the decline was a change in climate, bringing cold, wet weather that reduced harvests and left people susceptible to famine and disease. And one of the worst diseases of the time was itself directly attributable to the bad weather – ergotism, also known as St Anthony's fire, caused by a fungus flourishing on the damp rye used by the hungry people to make their bread.

The ergot fungus contains a poison that attacks the human central nervous system. Less than 2 per cent of the affected grains baked into bread causes any or all of: hallucinations, convulsions, abortion, gangrene leading to loss of limbs and even death. Whole village populations would suffer, with animals also being affected.

Ergotism became less common as the weather shifted out of the run of cold, damp conditions and as patterns of diet changed, favouring white bread and potatoes as staples. But it was still a problem in Russia early in the twentieth century and it played a part in the turmoil leading up to the French Revolution.

Bad weather and bad harvests are widely recognised as contributing to the unrest among French peasants in 1789. A further complication was a severe ergot infestation of the rye crop in Brittany that year, creating hallucinations among both peasants and landowners and leading to a widespread irrational fear that bandits were coming to steal their property and crops.

Related problems may still be relevant. There is an illness known as Kuru ('laughing disease') that affects the Fore tribe of Papua New Guinea, and is commonly thought to be caused by a virus passed on by cannibalism. Regina Schoental of the Royal Veterinary College has, however, suggested that it may in fact be caused by another mould that flourishes in the damp conditions of the New Guinea highlands.

The decline in Kuru since the 1950s might therefore be due not to a decline in cannibalism, but to changing weather patterns. So maybe the greenhouse effect does have a silver lining.

*The weather has connections with many areas
of fundamental science, some far from
obvious.*

The twinkling of stars in the dark night sky is not a sign
that the stars themselves are burning erratically, changing
their brightness from second to second. Rather, it is caused
by changes in the atmosphere overhead, as the light passing
through is distorted by layers of air at different temperatures and by the turbulence of the atmosphere.

The amount of twinkling, and even the colours of the
stars, are affected by the amount of turbulence, by the
composition of the atmosphere and by its temperature.
And this means that twinkling can, in the right circumstances, be a reliable indicator that rain is on the way.

In effect, the light that reaches the surface of the Earth
is being distorted by constantly shifting 'lumps' of air overhead. This is why most astronomical observatories are
located high on mountain ranges – the less air there is
overhead, the less twinkling and the better the observing
conditions for star watchers.

For people watching from the ground, especially in tropical regions, the twinkling itself is well worth observing. An
increased amount of twinkling is caused by strong winds in
the upper atmosphere carrying different parcels of air
across the line of sight, and by increased convection, in
which warm air near the surface rises and cools.

Another factor is humidity. The more moisture the air
contains, the more twinkling you will see, and as a bonus,
the extra moisture affects the starlight by making it appear
more blue.

Increased humidity is an obvious factor associated with
imminent rainfall. Increased convection is also likely to
bring rain, since it carries the moist air high into the atmosphere, where the air cools and the moisture forms clouds.

Even the build-up of upper atmosphere winds can be a sign of changing weather patterns, especially the onset of the monsoon.

So in sub-tropical regions at the end of the dry season, look out for increased twinkling of stars, with a diamond-blue edge to the twinkling. The rains will surely follow soon.

Albert Einstein's fame as the father of relativity theory rather obscures the fact that he was something of a poly-math. He also contributed, of course, to that other great pillar of twentieth-century physics, the quantum theory. But did you know that his PhD thesis actually explains rather well what happens in a cup of sweet tea? Or that it was Einstein, in 1910, who proved once and for all why the sky is blue?

We are so used to the fact that blue light comes to us from all over the sky that few people stop to wonder where the light comes from. If our light comes from the Sun, and light travels in straight lines, why isn't the bright Sun set in a black sky?

The answer is that sunlight has got scattered by the atmosphere of the Earth, bounced around until it comes at us from all directions. But sunlight doesn't get scattered evenly.

The first steps towards explaining the puzzle were taken by John Tyndall, the Irish physicist who succeeded Michael Faraday as Director of the Royal Institution in 1867. Two years later he discovered the 'Tyndall effect', by which large particles in solution scatter a beam of light shone into the liquid.

Tyndall – who was also one of the first people to investigate the carbon dioxide greenhouse effect – guessed that something similar happens in the atmosphere, with sun-light being scattered by dust particles suspended in the air. Sunlight itself contains all the colours of the rainbow, but experiments showed that short wavelength (blue) light is scattered more easily than longer wavelength (red) light.

In fact, the dust scattering invoked by Tyndall nicely explains why sunsets are red. But it does not explain why the sky is blue. To do that much scattering requires a very large number of very small particles – atoms and molecules. It was Einstein who put the right numbers into the calculation, explaining why the sky is blue and providing proof that air really is made of molecules, something that still needed proof, in the eyes of some scientists, at the end of the first decade of the twentieth century.

We are often asked to explain curious sights in the sky. Sometimes we see them ourselves, as happened one June evening. With the Sun about 25 degrees above the horizon and partly obscured by cloud, between 20 and 25 degrees to the right of the Sun there was a rainbowlike spectrum of colours, with a bright light beside it, visible for about ten minutes.

This is a classic example of what is known as a 'Sun-dog', part of a family of phenomena caused by ice crystals in the clouds bending light from the Sun. The six-sided ice crystals bend the light rays, by refraction, through an angle of 22 degrees.

Under ideal conditions, the result is a ring or halo of light around the Sun, making a circle that will just about fit around your two fists, held out together at arm's length and touching one another.

If the cirrus cloud responsible for this phenomenon is patchy, it will produce only a partial halo, and when the Sun is low in the sky, shining through well-broken cirrus clouds, this may result in two bright patches, one either side of the Sun, or a single bright patch, often rainbow-coloured, to one side.

But why a dog? The reason for the name is lost in the mists of time, but one suggestion is that it is because the coloured patch very often has a long horizontal streak of white light sticking out at one end, like a dog's tail.

If there are enough ice crystals in the right place, they can reflect so much sunlight that they create a Sun pillar, a beam of sunlight pointing vertically upwards from the rising or setting Sun and looking rather like the beam of a searchlight. And there is a related halo phenomenon, also caused by reflection rather than refraction, which is worth investigating.

Try standing with your back to the Sun, early in the morning, so that your shadow falls across a tightly mown lawn soaked with dew. If you are lucky, you will see a bright halo around the head of your shadow, strikingly like the halo supposed to surround the head of a saint: the nearest most of us will ever get to being canonised!

Other phenomena we have yet to see for ourselves, although we have it on impeccable authority that they do happen.

How can an icicle grow upwards, defying the law of gravity, from the surface of a frozen bowl of water? This burning question filled the correspondence columns of *Weather*, the house magazine of the Royal Meteorological Society, with puzzled enquiries, accompanied by photographic evidence, from as far afield as Norway.

The answer, it seems, it related to the curious property of water that means it expands when it freezes, taking up more room as solid ice than it did in the form of liquid water. It is only because of this that ice floats: if ice were more dense than water, as most solids are more dense than their liquid counterparts, it would form at the *bottom* of a lake, or the sea, not on the top.

Usually, when ice does form as a layer on the surface of water, the layer is uneven, and there are many weak spots, especially around the edges. As more of the water beneath the ice layer freezes, and therefore expands, it pushes water out through the weak spots, where it usually freezes in the normal fashion.

Just occasionally the layer of ice on the surface may be very even and frozen firmly to the edges of its container (a bird-bath is the classic example, although the effect has been seen even on puddles). In those circumstances, as the pressure builds up beneath the ice, water may begin to escape through a single weak spot in the surface layer. It will form a little dome of ice, containing liquid water, which grows steadily upwards as the pressure increases and repeatedly bursts through the weak spot on top.

The overall effect is like a frozen volcano, with water under pressure running up a narrow channel inside the growing ice spike, bursting out in a tiny eruption and dribbling down the sides to set like rocks solidifying out of molten magma.

The spikes of ice produced in this way are nearly always either circular or elliptical in cross-section, although as the exception that proves the rule *Weather* published one picture of a wedge-shaped ice pyramid, 5 cm high, that emerged in a bird-bath in Henley-on-Thames on 7 February 1988. The more usual spikes can reach heights of 15 cm.

*Weather watching is no longer restricted to
observations from the ground or even from
within the atmosphere of our planet.*

How do the weather forecasters on TV manage to get
pictures of 'our' part of the world whenever they need
them from satellites orbiting the Earth? As a satellite zips
along its orbit, surely it will be overhead only for a few
minutes at a time, at widely spaced intervals? This is not
much use if you want continuous cover of the weather
over, say, Britain; but there is a trick.

Because the Earth rotates once on its axis every day
(actually, once every 23 hours 56 minutes and 4.1 seconds)
a satellite in just the right orbit, taking the same time to
travel once around the centre of the Earth, will seem to
hover over one particular spot on the equator.

The speed with which a satellite orbits the Earth depends
on its altitude, but not in an obvious way. If you were in
an orbiting satellite and fired the rocket motors to slow
the satellite, you might expect it to fall in towards the
Earth. In fact, slower orbits are further out; you have to
speed up in the orbit to get closer to Earth. So while early
satellites such as Sputnik zipped around the Earth just
above the atmosphere in about ninety minutes, the Moon
takes a month to complete an orbit.

The right orbit for keeping watch on one part of the
Earth is known as a synchronous (or geostationary) orbit,
and it lies at a distance of 35,900 km from the Earth. The
idea of geostationary satellites was first put forward by
Arthur C. Clarke in the 1940s, but was not practicable
before the 1960s.

A satellite in a geostationary orbit precisely over the
equator seems to hang in one place on the sky. If the orbit
is slightly tilted, the satellite seems, from the Earth, to trace
out a figure of eight pattern once every twenty-four hours.

Geostationary orbits are highly valuable pieces of space 'real estate', and are rapidly becoming filled with communications satellites and weather satellites. A satellite such as the Geostationary Operational Environment Satellite (GOES) can study the Earth below, using optical and infrared sensors. They are especially good at monitoring cloud cover, and GOES itself has provided early warning of hurricanes approaching populated regions.

Equally, information about the weather can come from (almost) any old piece of wood.

What kind of person would be more interested in the frame of an Old Master than in the painting itself? It just might be a climatologist, because the wood used to make that frame could provide a valuable clue to the weather of the past, if it contains a distinctive pattern of tree rings.

Using tree rings to look back in time is nothing new. As the rings are laid down year by year, a slice cut from a freshly felled tree provides a set of rings which can be counted and dated, so that the ring laid down in the year of the Battle of Trafalgar, for example, can be identified and labelled.

The rings also vary in width from year to year, and by and large a wide ring means that the weather was good for growing that year, while a narrow ring points to a difficult growing season.

The classic use of tree rings to indicate past weather involves the long-lived bristlecone pine of the White Mountains of California. There, 'bad' weather for trees generally means cold. Some of these trees have been growing for more than 4,500 years, and a pencil-slim core of wood drilled from a living tree shows patterns of temperature changes over the centuries.

In the lowlands of a temperate country such as Britain,

'bad' weather for trees generally means dry weather. There are no trees in Britain as long-lived as the bristlecone pine, but the patterns of thick and thin rings in some samples are almost as distinctive as fingerprints.

'Dendrochronologists' and 'dendroclimatologists' (as researchers in this esoteric field are known) can match up the patterns of broad and narrow annual rings at the older end of samples from living wood with the outer layers of still older dead wood and so on in overlapping pieces back in time.

This is where the Old Masters come in. The key to the technique is to have well-dated samples of old wood to calibrate the chronology – and what better than a sliver from a picture frame surrounding a canvas that was painted in a known year?

The English obsession isn't really with the weather but with rain; which brings us to that other English obsession, cricket.

Cricket lovers rarely appreciate heavy rain during a test match (except, sometimes, when England are batting against the West Indies), but it is likely that it was rain that caused what is now the Oval ground, venue of the last test match each season, to remain an open space for so long. Nicholas Barton, in his book *The Lost Rivers of London*, writes that the River Effra (after which Effra Road and Effra Parade in south London were named), running through Stockwell and Kennington, used to be highly prone to flooding. Any reasonably heavy fall of rain would fill the basements of local houses, making life a misery.

The River Effra flowed, 12 feet wide and 6 feet deep, down the east side of Brixton Road to Kennington church along the south side of the Oval. There it joined up with a small tributary from the north before passing close to the old

Vauxhall Pleasure Gardens, under South Lambeth Road and joining the Thames at Vauxhall Bridge. The effects of rainfall on the Effra were so extreme that during the seventeenth century a bridge over it became 'prostrate and throwne down' by the 'enundacion and outrage of waters'.

All this proved a most effective way of keeping the area around the present-day Oval an open space. The entire area around the lower half mile of the Effra held little attraction for builders and house buyers because it was constantly liable to violent and sudden flooding. So the area easily avoided development and became just the place for central Londoners to play and watch cricket. In 1880, when the Effra was closed in, raised banks for spectators were built up using the excavated soil.

About the same time, Surrey Commissioners of sewers laid a tunnel to bring water directly from the Thames to store in newly built filter-bed reservoirs. These were so effective that they were said to 'render the water transparent'. The famous gasholder near the Oval was built on the site of one of these circular reservoirs.

The next time you see them pulling over the rain covers, remember that if it wasn't for the effect of heavy rain, the Oval could well not be there at all.

When it does come on to rain at a cricket match, the latest scientific evidence tells you the best way to head for cover.

The old puzzle of whether it is better to run for shelter when caught in rain or to saunter slowly towards cover seemed to have been resolved recently. A team from the University of Reading carried out a detailed analysis that concluded, to the surprise of many, that the best pace to travel at is just over 3 metres a second, a little more than walking pace. But they left unanswered the question of why, in that case, the instinctive reaction of most people is to run when caught in the rain.

It is hard to find fault with their mathematical analysis. The team compared the amount of rain falling on top of a person's head with the amount swept up by the front of their body as they moved forward, and allowed for different rates of rainfall. Admittedly, there were simplifications in their mathematical model. The person getting wet was regarded as a vertical cylinder, and the rainfall came straight down from the clouds, not slanting at an angle. Then, the total wetness of the cylindrical person was calculated for a journey of 100 metres through the rain, at different speeds (up to 8 metres a second) and for light rain, average rain or heavy rain.

Under all conditions, it turns out that if you stand still or move very slowly towards shelter you get very wet. At first, the quicker you move the less wet you get, because it takes less time to reach shelter. But by the time you are moving at 3 metres a second, you end up no wetter than if you run at 8 metres a second. For running speeds, the extra water swept up by your front cancels out the benefit of having less fall on your head.

So why *do* people run in the rain? The Reading team seems to have forgotten one important difference between mathematical cylinders and real people. People like to get indoors quickly and take their wet things off. Whatever the equations say, you won't find us dawdling when the next cloudburst occurs.

And we can't leave you without a mention of everybody's favourites – the dinosaurs.

Even if they could be cloned from blood inside mosquitoes trapped in amber, would Jurassic dinosaurs really thrive on Earth today? Leaving aside the question of how they would like our climate – much cooler than they knew – such creatures might find the air today quite unlike the stuff they were used to.

The Jurassic period was from about 190 to 139 million years ago. Ferns and cycads were common plants, while the first flying reptiles (pterosaurs) and first primitive bird (Archaeopteryx) appeared.

This raises a strange problem. According to modern reconstructions, both the pterosaurs and Archaeopteryx would have difficulty flying. They could probably have succeeded as gliding and soaring flyers, but getting airborne would have been no easy trick.

Various solutions to the puzzle have been proposed. One is that the flying reptiles may have hung about on cliff edges, like great bats, dropping off and spreading their wings to zoom across the waves of the Jurassic ocean.

But there is another possibility, linked with evidence of warmth in Jurassic times. Various pieces of evidence show that the equivalent of modern tropical climate extended to latitude 45°, where we find Minneapolis, Ottawa, Turin and Vladivostok today. Even allowing for other causes of climate change, one likely reason for this is that the atmosphere was much richer in carbon dioxide then, with a stronger greenhouse effect.

A thicker atmosphere, of course, would make it easier for gliding flyers to maintain altitude. Could it be that this is why pterosaurs and Archaeopteryx thrived in the Jurassic period, but would struggle to get off the ground today?

The answer may yet be forthcoming. Along with insects trapped in pieces of amber from the period, there are bubbles of air. Extracting and analysing these air bubbles without contamination has so far proved difficult. There is also the question of whether the air in the bubbles has reacted chemically with the amber over the past few score million years. But, just possibly, one day we may know for sure what kind of air Jurassic dinosaurs breathed, and flew through.

INDEX